A Small Dose of Medicine

by
James Griffin

First published by Barny Books

ISBN No: 978.1.903172.88.9

Publishers: Barny Books
                   Hough on the Hill
                   Grantham
                   Lincolnshire
                   NG32 2BB

                   Tel: 01400 250246
                   www.barnybooks.biz

Other titles by this author

A spoonful of Medicine   ISBN No: 1.903172.43.8
The Makings of a Doctor   ISBN No: 978.1.903172.76.6

This book is dedicated
to my late father
who taught me
the Art of Medicine

Contents

Contents

Mrs Connolly's Constipation

It isn't every day you get the chance to save the world but it once happened to me. I don't want to sound presumptuous but I think I may have prevented a world war or at the very least, a serious international conflict and it was all because of Mrs Connolly's constipation.

It's all about the "knock on effect" - that's when something triggers off a series of events that eventually cause a calamity. Napoleon said a loose button on one of his soldier's tunics could cost him a battle and we all know the story about the loose nail on the horse's shoe. Because of the nail, the shoe was lost and so on until the kingdom was lost and all because of that nail. And there's the saying, "A butterfly fluttering its wings in China can start a tornado in Florida."

It's all about the ripples that spread out from a single incident or action and that is exactly what happened when Mrs Connolly became constipated.

Mrs Connolly was a prim and proper widow of eighty. There would definitely never have been any buttons missing from her coat. She lived with her daughter, Angela, in the neatest house in all of Clonavon.

Angela, was a pleasant woman who worked for the Civil Service. When she wasn't working, she was at home in the house or garden following Mrs Connolly's precise instructions to the letter and dealing with her many ailments and medications with good humour. It didn't seem much of a life but Angela never complained. She was a woman of enormous patience. I think one of the things that kept her going was smoking.

Every evening, when her mother had gone to bed, Angela went into her back garden and smoked two cigarettes. She stayed outside for twenty minutes or half an hour at peace and in perfect harmony with the world. I know that smoking is bad for you but I think it was good for Angela.

When Mrs Connolly's lifelong constipation took a turn for the worst, even that little pleasure had to be given up. Her mother demanded Angela's attention every waking hour. Angela's two cigarettes a day had given her a little bit of free time, what we call protected time nowadays. As a result of the loss of that little protected time and the unending demands her mother made on her, Angela started to go down that roller coaster of anxiety and depression. She became irritable and the longer her mother's constipation lasted, the more irritable she became.

Mrs Connolly had been brought up in the Victorian era when people were obsessed with their bowels. Every Friday night was dosing night when children were given some concoction that would keep their bowels open. Brimstone and treacle was often used. Other parents chose syrup of figs. Mrs Connolly was given large doses of castor oil. Her mother and grandmother preferred castor oil because it did not limit them to giving it one day a week. The more they poured the stuff down the young Mrs Connolly's reluctant throat, the better her bowels worked and the happier the two women were.

As a result of all this unnecessary medication, Mrs Connolly's bowels got used to doing very little work at an early age. She developed a lazy bowel and that was solely through the silly behaviour of her mother and grandmother.

As she grew older, she needed more and more castor oil for her bowel to work at all. By the time she reached her teens, a bottle of castor oil didn't go too far with her. It was

8

disappearing down her throat every two days with little effect. She was moved on to something stronger as well as being force-fed brown bread, green vegetables, plenty of prunes and porridge. That just about kept her bowels working. By the time she married and escaped from her mother's clutches she had taken such an aversion to laxative inducing food, she refused to eat another slice of brown bread or touch a prune.

With advances in medicine and the nation's preoccupation with their bowels, new medications for constipation were being introduced all the time, just as well for Mrs Connelly because, by then, she badly needed them.

By the time Mrs Connelly reached seventy, she was almost overdosing herself on laxatives several times a day. She had tried every available one in the United Kingdom and further afield as well. She had a daughter in America who sent her parcels of the stuff, every laxative that had ever been produced there and every laxative that was known to man. When her daughter ran out of all the preparations that country could provide, she persuaded a friend who lived in South America to send her homeopathic remedies and other exotic medicines used by the Inca tribes.

Despite all this, Mrs Connelly's constipation kept building up to a crisis point every few months. I could see by the increasingly frequent calls I was receiving from Angela we were about to have a red alert on our hands if something wasn't done about Mrs Connelly's constipation.

I was in the middle of surgery one morning when Angela phoned. She sounded desperate.

"Dr Griffin, I'm sorry to interrupt you during surgery. I know you've been doing your best for my mother but something has got to be done about her constipation before she drives me and everybody in Clonavon completely mad."

Angela was speaking so rapidly I could barely make her out. It was as if a floodgate had opened and a torrent of pent up frustration released. "I hardly dare show my face in the chemist shop any more. As soon as Ballantine sees me, he stops his singing and a look of, "I wish I'd left 10 mintues ago," comes over his face. It's not hard to figure out why. I've pestered him so much over the past six weeks about getting new laxatives for my mother. I hate pestering him but, if I don't, my mother gives me no peace. She pesters me to pester him. Day and night it's the same old tune. 'Go and see if Ballantine has anything for my bowels.' It's the only thing I ever hear and it's driving me crazy."

I tried to interrupt and tell Angela I'd call and see her after morning surgery but I couldn't get a word in edgeways as she hurtled on.

"I don't blame Ballantine for never wanting to see me again as long as he lives but it's the only way I can get any peace and get my mother to shut up about her constipation. I know I upset him and his staff with my demands and I know he's phoned all sorts of places to try and help me out. He's done all he can. It's ridiculous beyond description. It ends up with everyone being upset and all because of my mother's mindless obsession about her stupid bowels." Angela sounded as if she was at the end of her tether. She was on the verge of tears as she went on.

"My life wouldn't be worth living if I didn't give in to her and do what she asks. All she ever thinks or talks about are those bowels of hers. If a little green man from Mars walked into the house, the only thing she would want to know would be the names of any good laxatives on Mars.

The line went silent as Angela spluttered to a halt. I tried to speak but only got two words out before she started again, faster than ever.

"Do you know what my mother wants now? It's unbelievable … she wants my sister Teresa to come home from America to help her get her bowels sorted out. Teresa trained as a nurse before she married but that was more than twenty years ago. She hasn't done any nursing since and knows and cares as much about constipation as Donald Duck's granny. Teresa is upset with all the fuss and doesn't know what to do. Her husband's a general in the American army and he doesn't want her to leave him with all the problems he's got on his hands at the moment. He's dealing with a crazy warmongering General at the White House and needs Teresa's support. She knows if she comes home, her husband won't be able to cope without her and that crazy General might get the better of him and persuade the President to start another war the way things are going and all because of mother and her ridiculous constipation." The line went silent as Angela dissolved into tears.

"Look Angela," I said, "I'll come and see your mother straight after surgery and we'll get this constipation problem sorted out one way or another. In the meantime go and get yourself a nice cup of tea and have a quiet cigarette. It'll help to settle you down."

Angela laughed ruefully.

"I can't even do that. Mother hasn't any idea I smoke. If she even smelt tobacco smoke on me, I think the shock might get her bowels working double quick, which mightn't be a bad thing come to think of it."

A couple of hours later, I parked my car outside their neat, white cottage. I walked up the paved path between beautiful flower borders and an immaculately cut laurel hedge. Angela opened the door. She was a good looking woman in her early forties. She seemed worn out by her mother's demands. As she brought me into the house, I noticed she had lost a lot of weight since I'd last seen her.

Mrs Connolly was propped up on a soft armchair in their pink and white sitting room. She had a small, mahogany table in front of her where several brown bottles were neatly arranged beside a dozen boxes of tablets. A quick glance told me they were all of the anti constipation type

She looked up as I came in. She must have been very good looking in her youth but her fine features were now etched with a certain haughtiness that would have put most people on their guard as soon as they met her. She was obviously used to getting her own way.

Her blue rinsed hair was neatly permed. She was dressed in blue-green tweed and pearls. A heavily jewelled engagement ring and an eternity ring were on her finger beside her wedding ring. Her nails were painted with bright red varnish. I could see by the alert look in her eyes, there wouldn't be any possibility of me pulling the wool over this woman's eyes.

"Thank you for calling, Dr Griffin," she said in a tight, precise voice. "Teresa, my daughter in America is just off the phone and she'll be calling back shortly about my problem. Now, in the meantime, have you any suggestions ?"

I was a bit taken back by her abrupt approach. Prof W.J.P.R.Soames, my professor of Medicine when I was a student had warned us about patients like Mrs Connolly. "Beware the blue rinse, red nails and heavy jewelry in former beauty queens, my young immature colleagues" he'd say in his rich plummy voice. "They can put you under a lot of pressure and bring on very bad Karma. Never let those ladies rush you

12

into making hasty decisions. You must always control the pace of the consultation until good Karma returns."

All of Prof Soames daft advice had a grain of truth in it, as in like right now. I had to stop Mrs Connolly pressurizing me. I needed a little time to sum up the situation.

"I think I may have some suggestions Mrs Connelly" I said "but I think it's essential I examine you first. If you don't mind, I'd like you to lie on your bed so I can carry out a proper abdominal examination and assess how serious your problem is."

She raised her eyebrows disapprovingly.

"I can assure you Dr Griffin, my problem is serious, very serious indeed." She reluctantly got to her feet and went into her bedroom. As she prepared herself, I opened the medical file I had brought along with me and flicked through it. I thought the easiest way of solving this dilemma would be to have her seen by a gastroenterologist or a bowel surgeon as soon as possible. As I flipped through her file, I came across a report from a consultant bowel surgeon dated six months earlier. I read the lengthy summary at the end of his long letter,

'This rather difficult lady has been assessed by me as an in-patient with constipation though I don't quite understand why she had to be admitted to hospital as an emergency for such a non urgent condition. All her investigations were entirely normal despite the patient's complete refusal to accept this or to even try to comprehend any explanations I offered her.

A sigmoidoscopy, colonoscopy, Barium meal, Barium enema, oesophagogastroduodenoscopy and multiple blood tests including a full blood count, liver function test, urea and electrolytes and biochemical profiles as well as a cholecystogram and an electrocardigram were all completely normal.

I have given Mrs Connolly practical advice about taking a healthy diet, such as eating prunes and wholemeal bread. She gave me the impression that she wasn't listening to a word I said and insisted (and I quote) "I would rather die than eat, brown bread or green vegetables or another prune of any description after the amount of them I was forced to eat as a young girl".

I advised her about taking regular exercise and a sufficient fluid intake.

She appeared to take no interest whatsoever in anything I said to her regarding diet, exercise or fluid intake and persisted in demanding "stronger tablets or medicine" insisting they were the only things that help her.

At the end of a rather fraught interview I concluded that Mrs Connolly takes inadequate roughage, fluid and exercise and that she has no intention of rectifying any of these deficiencies. I am afraid if her problem recurs, I have little in the way of help I can offer this lady and would suggest you refer her to one of my colleagues or to another hospital."

"Or to the North Pole or Pluto as far as you are concerned, Mr Bowel Surgeon" I thought as I finished reading his letter. Mr Bowel Surgeon never wanted to see Mrs Connolly again in this life or the next, nor would any of his colleagues after reading that discharge letter. That didn't seem to leave me with too many options for referral. I was on my own.

I put the file down, took a deep breath and went in to examine Mrs Connelly. Her abdomen was soft as one would have expected in somebody of her age. It was easy to palpate. To my surprise I felt a massive back log of constipation that filled the entire left side of her abdomen almost up as far as the lower rib cage on the left side.

"So you are a genuine case after all" I thought as I listened to her abdomen with my stethoscope. "It looks like her bowel is going to need a stick of dynamite or, at least, a colonic wash out to get this lot shifted. How did that bowel surgeon manage to find everything normal when he saw her six months ago? He must have examined her on one of her good days – as in just after she emptied her bowel out of a three week build up. Why do consultants always have to see patients when they're at their best?" It was one of the recurring problems G.P's have to put up with that's completely exasperating – patients with genuine long term problems having entirely normal results after hospital investigations."

There wasn't much chance of Mrs Connolly having a wash out at the hospital after the surgeon's comments. He seemed as though he'd had all he could take of Mrs Connelly and her constipation.

"You've tried a Fletchers enema, Mrs Connolly, have you?" I asked hopefully.

"You might as well give me hard putty as that stuff. It made me worse, ten times worse," she said sharply as if thinking of what other silly suggestions was I going to come up with next. She watched me through her gimlet eyes as I racked my brain for inspiration. Just then, the phone rang, I gave a sigh of relief. I was off the hook for a few moments at least or so I thought.

Mrs Connolly picked up the receiver then passed it across to me.

"Teresa wants a word with you," she snapped.

I took the phone and hoped this wasn't going to be the twenty question inquisition which you sometimes get when relatives phone from abroad. That was something I could do without. "What are you doing for my mother / granny /

15

daughter in law? My doctor over here in Cape Town / New York / Timbuktu says she should be getting such and such a treatment and why are you not giving it to them," and so on until you feel your ears burning and your head throbbing.

To my relief a pleasant, soft voice spoke. There was no doubting the strain Teresa was feeling. She spoke so quietly, almost in a whisper, I had to strain my ears to hear her.

"Hello Dr Griffin, this is Teresa Schwartz, Mrs Connolly's daughter phoning from Washington. I'm sorry to take up your time but I'm sure you're aware from what Angela has told you my mother is demanding I come home to sort out her constipation. I'm sure you know as well as I do why her constipation started in the first place and how she doesn't help herself with her diet of chocolate and cornflakes.

"She killed my poor father with her bowel obsession. He took a heart attack in the end. He couldn't stand hearing any more about it. I thought when I was growing up that all women were constipated and I would have to face it myself. Fortunately my father absolutely refused to let my mother give us castor oil when we were young even though he was afraid of her tantrums and sulks."

I liked the sound of this woman. She sounded so sensible. No wonder her husband didn't want her to leave him when he was in the middle of a crisis.

"Now Doctor," Teresa went on, "I know mother is right beside you and trying to hear every word I'm saying. That's why I'm speaking so quietly."

I glanced round at Mrs Connolly. If ears could have grown and bent round corners, hers would have done just that. She had cocked her good ear towards the phone and was concentrating so ferociously to hear what was being said, she didn't notice I was looking at her.

"I'm in a dilemma at the moment. I think Angela gave you some idea of what's going on. My husband is completely stressed out and I'm the only one who can keep him going. He works at the Pentagon and is an adviser to the President. When I told him two days ago my mother wanted me to come home and help out with her constipation, he threw a wobbly. I can't repeat what he said but the gist of it was there's no way he wants me to come back to Clonavon now and certainly not for mother's constipation. I think if the British Prime Minister and all his cabinet were suffering from terminal constipation, his answer would still be the same.

Since I told him about mother wanting me back, he's been like a bear with a sore head, shouting at everyone at home and probably at work too. When he gets like that, I wouldn't put it past him to shout at that General or the President and that wouldn't be a good thing, the way things are at the moment. If I could just tell him you are dealing with Mother's constipation and there's no need for me to come home he'd revert to his usual big teddy bear self and get on with his job of trying to keep the peace. Than all the red lights and alert buttons around the Pentagon could be switched off and everything would be peaceful again, if you see what I mean."

I was stunned. I suddenly realized how important Mrs Connolly's constipation really was. My handling of this situation could make a difference not just to her but to world peace. It was the moment I had dreamed about and had been waiting for all my life, when I single handedly would save the world.

I was barely able to control the excitement in my voice as I reassured Teresa that I would sort everything out. There would be no doubt about that, no doubt whatsoever. There would be no need for her to come home. She thanked me profusely.

"You've no idea what a relief that is to me Dr Griffin," she said, "Thank you, thank you so much, I'll never forget your kindness. I can't tell you how relieved my husband will be when he hears I'm not going to leave him on his own."

When I put the phone down, Mrs Connolly didn't look quite so happy.

"What do you mean telling Teresa there is no need for her to come home," she almost snarled. "She's needed here to look after me. As far as I'm concerned, she can forget about that clown of a husband of hers and his tin soldiers and their little worries. What about my constipation? It's more important than anything going on over there."

I was taken aback by her anger, though I've found over the years that old people fall broadly into one of two groups. They either end up being completely self centred like Mrs Connolly or they only think of the needs of others.

Mrs Connolly was not remotely concerned about the possibility of inter continental ballistic missiles being launched. I had to ignore her anger and focus myself on constipation and world peace. There was now a huge responsibility on my young shoulders

I needed to think long and hard and come up with something to sort this mess out. I had the vaguest feeling in the back of my mind that I knew the answer to this constipation conundrum but for the life of me, I just couldn't get the answer to come into my consciousness. I knew there was the name of some medicine at the outer limits of my memory that would resolve this problem but no matter how hard I tried, I couldn't remember what that medicine was called. Sometimes when I have memory lapses like that, the name will come in to my head in a flash. At other times the first letter will appear in my minds eye and the word will develop slowly after that. For

18

example, if I have forgotten a man's name and say his name is Boris, then the letter B will come to mind and, slowly, the rest of the name will follow.

That was what happened to me then. The letter P came into my consciousness and I knew it was important. I concentrated and tried to think what came after P but nothing seemed to come from the fog of my memory. Would it ever come in time to sort out this crisis? Suddenly the word came to me like a thunderbolt. The word was pig. I was so pleased, I shouted it out, 'PIG! Pig, yes it's pig. The word is pig'.

Mrs Connolly looked startled. I ignored her angry snort as I concentrated again. I knew 'pig' wasn't the full answer. There was another word, a word to describe pig but I couldn't think of it. As I concentrated, oblivious to my surroundings, I could feel the dark clouds beginning to part. And then it came to me ...... constipated. That was it, that was the word I needed to remember to describe the pig. Constipated pig. That was it.

"Constipated pig, constipated pig, that's it, I remember it now. Constipated pig," I repeated excitedly, almost at the top of my voice. Angela and Mrs Connolly were looking at me. Then Angela started to laugh, quietly at first then louder and louder until her shoulders were shaking but Mrs Connolly didn't laugh – in fact quite the opposite. She looked extremely cross.

"How dare you call me a constipated pig, you impertinent young man? How dare you! Who do you think you are? I'll have you reported for insolence. You call yourself a doctor? You're no doctor. You're an excuse for a doctor. You're not fit to look after a dead donkey never mind my constipation."

In my effort to concentrate, I'd forgotten Mrs Connelly was in the room. I suddenly realized my blunder.

"No, no, no, Mrs Connolly," I exclaimed. "No not at all. I'm not calling you a constipated pig. No, no. I wouldn't dream of that. It's not like that at all. It's just that I was thinking about a friend of mine who had a, had a...." It was my turn to splutter. I didn't think Mrs Connolly would like to hear the true story of what I'd just remembered. In fact I was sure she wouldn't. I had to rack my brain to come up with something to placate her.

"This friend of mine I was just thinking about when I shouted out just then and I'm really very sorry about that, well, em, he, em, he lives on a farm in the South of Ireland. He was em, em" – this was getting difficult- "got em, constipated and people said he was a constipated pig because his surname was Bacon, if you see what I mean. Bacon, pig, you see the connection?" I could see the story was pathetic and wasn't being received too well either. "But the point of all this is, the story that is ..... it ah, it ah had a happy ending. This man you see, the Mr Bacon I just mentioned, well he had the worst constipation I ever heard of and he, he got some tablets from France which did the trick, so to speak. They sorted out his terrible constipation. Nothing in Britain or America would shift it but the French ones did."

Mrs Connolly looked at me suspiciously.

"What are the names of those tablets, then?" she demanded.

That was the problem. I couldn't remember. There wasn't even the glimmer of a letter to help me.

I thought for a moment about that constipated pig. A friend of mine at University was a farmer's son from County Meath. He told me once his father bred prize pigs and sold them worldwide. On one occasion his father was having desperate problems with one of his best medal winning porkies. The pig was constipated and not doing too well despite the attention of two of the best vets in the country and a couple of bucketfuls of laxatives everyday into the bargain.

The problem was solved when his daughter came home from a holiday in France with a packet of laxatives she had bought there. She said they were much too strong for her altogether. They had ended up giving her "the runs". She suggested her father try them out on his prize porkie. As soon as the pig was given two of the tablets, he had instant relief. The problem was, I couldn't remember the name of those tablets. I hadn't seen my friend for well over a year, since he finished his studies and went back to his father's farm.

Mrs Connolly continued to eye me with that suspicious look in her eye while I thought desperately. It was useless. I hadn't the vaguest idea of what the name of those tablets was.

"Look, Mrs Connolly," I said with an optimism I didn't feel, "I have a friend who got the tablets from France. He lives in County Meath. I'll phone him tonight and let you know what they're called tomorrow."

"How will you get those tablets over from France in time for me even if you do find out their name?" she asked imperiously.

"We'll sort that out tomorrow," I told her as I grabbed my medical bag and left.

Angela was laughing silently as I left. She was wiping tears from her eyes and couldn't speak. At least somebody was happy.

I went back and did the evening surgery. Afterwards I climbed into the attic and scanned the books and notes I had brought back from Dublin, all seven years worth of them looking for my friend Tom's telephone number. After a couple of hours, I looked at the last possible place where his number might be, my brief case, and there it was, right at the bottom.

Why is it that the last place you look is always where you find what you have sometimes spent days searching for? Perhaps it was time I set up a new filing system.

I phoned Tom's number immediately. His father answered.

"I'm sorry young lad, but he's gone to Perth for six months," Mr Morrison replied jovially. "He only left three weeks ago."

I sighed. Just my luck. Gone to Perth, when I needed to talk to him.

"Would you have his telephone number in Australia, by any chance, Mr Morrison?" I asked anxiously.

"I think I've got it here somewhere," he mumbled. "Hold on a minute. I'll go and have a look. You know the wife usually deals with that end of things." He put the phone down.

I prayed his filing system would be better than mine. It wasn't. I could hear paper rustling and his voice muttering directions to himself. Eventually, ten minutes later when I was beginning to lose the will to live, he picked up the phone and, laboriously, read out the number to me. He got it right on the third attempt.

"You don't happen to know what time it is out in Perth?" I asked. "I don't want to phone Tom in the middle of the night."

"I haven't a baldy, young lad. The wife deals with all that sort of thing. It's her that usually does the phoning. She's out at the Bingo. She always goes to the Bingo on a Thursday night and sometimes on a Tuesday too." Then he went on to tell me in great detail about his wife's Bingo career.

After twenty minutes, I thought I'd heard all I ever wanted to know about Bingo for the rest of my life.

"If you don't mind, Mr Morrison I'll just have to leave you there and maybe catch you another time when I get the chance to hear some more about that big Bingo jackpot win back in 1964. It sounds really interesting."

I put the phone down and roared like a bull for a minute to relieve my pent up frustration. Then I started searching for an atlas. I needed to have some idea of international date lines if I was to phone Tom. Eventually I found the atlas under the sofa. I must have left it there when I'd been looking to find out how to spell Azerbaijan to finish a crossword puzzle. Perth was eight hours ahead of us. It was half past five in the morning over there. I didn't want to phone Tom in the middle of the night especially about a constipated pig he'd probably forgotten about anyway. I sat up until after midnight before I phoned.

A very sleepy voice answered.

"Hello, Tom," I said cheerfully. "I thought you'd be wide awake at this time of the morning, you know, all bright eyed and bushy tailed and rearing to go."

"Is that you James?" Tom sounded cross. "Why are you phoning me at this time of the morning? I'm working night shifts. I've only just gone to sleep."

"You can't win them all," I thought. "I'd better get straight to the point then, Tom. I'm sorry I've woken you but I need to know something that's very important to me. I know it might seem an odd thing to call you about, especially at this time in the morning and all the way to Australia as well but do you, by any chance, remember the time when your father's prize pig, Miss Piggy was constipated?"

My question was followed by a long silence.

"Look James," he eventually said. He sounded angry and perplexed. "I know I haven't spoken to you for a long time but can you tell me if you've been feeling well recently? You know, getting out and about, not letting things get on top of you, not working too hard? Maybe it's time you thought about taking a bit of a break, relaxing yourself, taking a holiday even and especially not phoning me about a Miss Piggy at this time of the morning."

"I know what you're thinking Tom and I know where you're coming from and I can understand all that and I know this sounds ridiculous but there's a woman in the village who is driving us all nuts...."

"This isn't one of your practical jokes, is it James?"

"No, no Tom, it isn't. I'm being serious, very serious and I'm sorry again for waking you but, I've got a woman in the village who is causing me no end of trouble." I was tempted to tell him World Peace was on the line. Then I thought the way he was feeling it maybe wasn't a good time to mention something so sensitive. "This woman is a patient of mine and she's very constipated and I can remember you telling me, it must have been three years ago now, about how your father's prize pig was in the same state and your sister Mary got something from France that pulled the pig through its constipation if you know what I mean."

As I blurted it out in one breath to stop Tom interrupting, I began to realise how stupid it must have sounded to him but it was very serious to me.

"Yes, I do sort of remember it but are you sure you're alright yourself James? Not feeling a bit strained or under the weather?"

"I've never felt better, Tom" I told him. "It's just that I'd love to know what you gave that pig so I can give some of the same treatment to this patient of mine."

He couldn't remember the name of the tablet. He could only just remember the incident but he did give me the telephone number of his sister Mary who now lived in France.

Then he gave me some more advice about slowing down. Chill out were his words. Before he put the phone down he said, "And I don't know what gave you the idea I'm in Australia, I'm up in Perth in Scotland."

"Up in Scotland?" I said in alarm.

"Only joking, James" he replied with a laugh. "Have you lost your sense of humour altogether? By the way you're going on about constipated pigs at this hour of the morning, you must have a serious humour failure yourself or you're becoming demented. Good night and keep taking your tablets if you can remember" he roared as he slammed the phone down.

It was a bit late to phone France then especially as they are an hour ahead of us. I set my alarm for seven and phoned Mary at eight o'clock, local time. Fortunately she remembered the name of the tablets straight away, Forlax. She sounded a bit surprised at my enquiry but promised to send me some over by express post that day and she did. I phoned her later and thanked her. I was about to tell her the part she had played in promoting world peace but then thought that might have only created more problems if she and Tom ever got together and started discussing me.

When the tablets arrived I took them straight over to Mrs Connolly. It's funny what excites some people but those tablets certainly excited Mrs Connolly more than if she had won the Sweepstakes, although she tried not to show it.

When I called a couple of days later, Angela brought me into the bathroom and proudly showed me the bedpan on the bathroom floor. It contained what one would expect a bedpan to contain, except an awful lot more. Angela was so relieved, she started to dance a little jig of joy around it and I joined in.

Mrs Connolly stopped complaining and everything returned to normal.

'That's General Practice for you,' I thought as I drove home. 'One minute you're saving the world and the next, you're dancing around a constipated bed pan.'

But the next month, Mrs Connolly's constipation was as bad as ever. Sometimes you can't win them all, not against constipation anyway.

Home Again

Looking back I think I didn't really know how important constipation was until I met Mrs Connolly. My first few weeks in Clonavon were a sharp learning curve.

As I settled back into my home village, I realized a lot had changed in the seven years since I'd left. I'd been a young, carefree student then with no responsibilities and full of excitement at the prospect of leaving home for the first time to study Medicine in Dublin.

I was a doctor now and doing a GP locum for my father while he took a break from thirty years of general practice. Life was a lot more serious.

I was the only doctor in the village and for a dozen miles around. There were no Dr O'Flatherties to bail me out if I got into trouble like there had been in my previous post in Kerry a month earlier. That had been an idyllic time, living alone in a rambling hilltop house with spectacular views of the Kerry mountains and the rolling Atlantic ocean during the hottest summer in living memory.

The attendance rate at the surgery had been the lowest on record as the villagers went salmon fishing or brought in bumper crops of hay. Four months of quiet surgeries with only the rare emergency left me time to walk in the hills and swim in the sea.

When I came back to Clonavon I soon realized life at home was going to be a lot less relaxed. The weather had taken a turn for the worse and it rained every day for two weeks. Rain has a way of bringing people to the surgery. I hardly had time to find my bearings. Fortunately my father stayed around for a few days.

It took time to settle in as the young village doctor with all its responsibilities. On top of everything else I had to get used to people who had called me James all my life now calling me Doctor and expecting me to behave like one. I could no longer gad about like an immature youth but had to conduct myself with a certain gravitas. My days of kicking a football in the village street with my friends or throwing stones into the Clonavon river were well and truly over. More sedate pursuits like taking Belle, the family retriever, for a walk were now the order of the day. That quiet life style was what people expected of their doctors in those days.

Every day, no matter what the weather, I put Belle on a lead and took her for a walk of rediscovery. We walked the fields and roads I'd roamed as a boy and through the streams and rivers I'd fished with my friends.

The village was quiet in the evenings. There was rarely any traffic. Groups of boys played football in the middle of the road just as I did when I was their age, always keeping an eye open for Sergeant Milligan doing his rounds on his bicycle. I walked for a long time, thinking of the past and, only then appreciating what a happy, carefree childhood I'd had in such peaceful surroundings.

Each day we'd cross the three arched bridge that spanned the Clonavon river and I'd look down to see if there were any trout in the water. I had spent countless days there with my friends, wading barefoot up and down in the water with our nets and jam jars looking for sticklebacks. We didn't go home until our stomachs were aching with hunger and our feet blue with cold.

Belle and I roamed the narrow roads peering over tall hedges at lush green fields. Occasionally she would pick up the scent of a rabbit or hare that made her yelp with excitement and bound off, usually in the wrong direction. No matter where I started I invariably found my feet drawing me towards the Hills of Crewe.

One bright sunny Autumn afternoon I stood at the top of the Hill of Crewe and looked at the scenery around me in admiration. I thought then I must have spent my childhood walking about with my eyes closed. How could I not have seen such beauty?

In front lay the distant sandy shores of Lough Neagh. To the North the blue peaks of the Sperrin Mountains rose spectacularly and to the South, the Mountains of Mourne swept down to the Irish Sea.

The silent Black Mountains were to the East and when I looked Westwards there was a rich tapestry of green and yellow and golden fields stretching for miles across the plains of Ulster.

After years of hearing nothing but noise and bustle in Dublin, I found the silence and slowness of Clonavon like a balm. It was as though I had moved back to a less hurried time.

The village hadn't changed since I left. In fact it hadn't changed in over a hundred years. It had one broad street reaching over the brow of the small hill and known for centuries as The Village of the Long Street. One of the followers of St Patrick founded a Church there in the fifth century beside the Clonavon River and the Church standing there today, St Andrews Church of Ireland, was built on that site.

The houses along the street were single storey and built from grey granite. The only businesses were a shop, a pharmacy and a pub although the pub always seemed closed. As a boy, I watched men in dark clothes and riding black bicycles coming to the pub. They would lean their bikes

29

against the wall and rap at the door. It would open just wide enough to admit them but we never saw who opened it or what was inside.

A man called Gilbert McSweeney ran the only shop in the village. He was a big, jolly man with a bushy beard. He always wore a collar and tie and a green shop coat. Everyone liked him. He was not a man to curse or say a bad word about anybody. His shop sold everything from pork chops and brandy balls, to Tilley lamps and diesel engines. If he didn't have what you wanted, he would get it for you by the end of the week. Children loved his shop. There was so much to explore and so many interesting things to find. It looked small from the front but the further you went into it, the more nooks and crannies you discovered where you could find all sorts of things hidden away. In the summer, Gilbert put up a red and white striped awning with flowers and gardening tools beneath it.

Just a couple of doors up from him was Ballantine's chemist shop. I used to watch Herbert Ballantine through the big glass windows making up pungent looking medicines from enormous green and brown bottles with strange names on them. He always sang as he mixed. He had a deep baritone voice you could hear the length of the street.

It was good to get home as dusk gathered and settle in front of a cosy fire with a cup of coffee and a paper for fifteen or twenty minutes before starting the evening surgery.

After a few days showing me the ropes, my parents left on their extended break. One of my brothers or sisters occasionally came home from college for a weekend but apart from that, I had the family home all to myself.

Our house was built on a hill just outside the village and surrounded by green fields. It had a long avenue up a steep hill that tested the lungs of any visitors. There was a front garden with two enormous cherry trees and numerous bushes and flower beds. The cherry trees blossomed in May with an explosion of palest pink. Later when the winds blew, the blossom drifted down like snow flakes and formed a thick carpet. My sisters gathered it in handfuls when they were young and threw it over each other like confetti. It was the perfect place to play games like hide and seek amongst the many bushes and deep undergrowth.

The back garden was more of a football pitch and bordered by a line of beech and ash trees which I often climbed as a boy. The remnants of a tree house my father once built for us was now reduced to a few haphazard planks. The garden had often echoed to the sounds of children shrieking and squealing with excitement as they chased each other and played football or rode their bikes over homemade ramps with their friends.

My father's surgery adjoined the house. It had two consulting rooms and a small waiting room that held eight people with the knees of those opposite each other almost touching. Anyone coming after that had to go back outside and stand on the steps until a seat became available. The ancient radio, high up on one wall, blared out either classical music or Irish country and western depending on who switched it on first.

For as long as I remembered the district nurse was Bella and the part time receptionist, Ida. At eleven o'clock every morning, my mother invited them in for tea and biscuits. We children had to stay outside and on no account were we to let out grubby hands stray anywhere near the District Nurse's biscuits.

Bella was a big hearted woman in her mid-fifties who had been born in the village. She trained in England before returning to Ireland, leaving behind a rich businessman who wanted to marry her. She preferred to go home and work as a mid-wife in the district. For twenty-five years my father and Bella delivered all the babies born in Clonavon at home, often under the light of a Tilley lamp. She knew all her patients intimately and they in turn loved her for her years of selfless service. I'd often see her in her distinctive blue uniform, driving around on her calls, smiling and waving to all the people she met.

Ida had been working for my father for twenty years when I went there as his locum. She was a small, plump woman in her mid-fifties with permed hair. She wore tweed clothes and sensible shoes. When she went out, even if it was only to McSweeney's shop, she put on a hat that looked like an upside down funnel. She spoke slowly, pronouncing every word carefully. When I first met her, I thought she was boring and humourless but, when I got to know her better, I realized I couldn't have been more wrong.

Before she came to work for my father, she was a librarian but gave up her job to look after her husband who was dying from cancer. Ida wasn't one of my father's patients but when he heard she was suffering from depression after the death of her husband, he immediately got into his car and went round to her house. He was always a very impulsive man. When she answered the door, he didn't give her a chance to speak.

"Ida," he said, "I need you to help me in the surgery as a part time receptionist and secretary."

She looked at him in amazement. "But I know nothing about being a medical secretary," she protested, "I'm a librarian."

"You know how to answer the phone and file charts, don't you?"

"Yes, I do."

"Can you type?"

"No, I can't."

"Well, you'll soon learn. I'll get you a couple of lessons. Mrs McBride's a great teacher of the typing and she'll soon have you typing quicker than quicksilver."

Ida was overwhelmed by my father's enthusiasm and persistence.

"What about Monday then?"

"What do you mean, what about Monday, Dr Griffin?"

"What I mean is, what about you starting on Monday in the surgery?"

"Monday?" Ida exclaimed. "You can't be serious, me starting on Monday, Doctor. It's too soon. I wouldn't be ready for it by then."

"There's nothing to get ready about Ida. You're a highly qualified woman. Alright then, you can start on Tuesday. I'll see you at nine o'clock. We'll sort your salary out later."

Before Ida could say a word, he'd jumped into his car and sped off.

My mother had been filling in as his secretary. She wasn't a bit pleased when she heard he'd appointed somebody else without even discussing it with her.

"You'll have no need to answer the phone or front door or hand out prescriptions any more Joan," he told her obviously pleased with himself. Despite his explanation, she felt she had been ousted from her role but Ida hadn't been in the surgery for an hour before my mother realized what an asset she was and what a burden had been taken off her shoulders.

Ida took to the job like a duck to water. She knew everyone in Clonavon, knew where they lived, who was married to who, the blood relationships between different families and everything that had happened there for almost a hundred years.

When I started doing my father's locum, I found her encyclopaedic knowledge invaluable especially for the first few months until I began to recognise and remember the different families and their connections myself.

Airport 1

I had never seen my parents so excited as they were when setting off on their holiday. They were like a couple of children going to the sea-side for the day.

As soon as they left, I started getting ready for my first day on my own. I was in for a shock. I went into the surgery at nine o'clock and it was full of children and their mothers. Another crowd was waiting outside on the steps. They had all come for their vaccinations. I felt overwhelmed. To make matters worse, Ida phoned to say she couldn't get her car to start and would be late.

It was in the days before pre-filled syringes and auxiliary staff. I had to do the lot myself - fill up the syringes after laboriously opening the thick glass vials with a file, double check the batch numbers, complete the vaccination forms, make a note on the charts, give all the injections and deal with the squealing children and their anxious mothers.

My father must have contacted about thirty mothers and told them to bring their children to the surgery that day - which explained why he had been in such a hurry to leave. He disliked vaccinations almost as much as I did.

I was half way through the queue of children when the phone rang. Fortunately Ida had just arrived and she answered it. She talked for a long time before coming back to tell me an official at Belfast City Airport was looking for a doctor immediately.

"That's got nothing to do with me, Ida" I said as I struggled to deal with a shrieking child. "There are plenty of other doctors nearer the airport. Why can't that smart alec official call one of them?"

Ida didn't speak for a minute. That had to be a bad sign. Ida was one of those wonderful women who always do their best to deflect flak away from their men-folk whether it's their father, husband or employer. I knew by the look on her face she hadn't been able to deflect this one.

"I'm sorry, James but none of the doctors around here wanted to be on call for this particular airline so they asked your father and he agreed to cover them only a month ago."

"He did what?" I almost shouted. "He never told me anything about that."

"Maybe he didn't want to upset you," Ida said soothingly.

"Didn't want to upset me?" I repeated. "Well, I'm telling you Ida, he's just gone and done that."

"Unfortunately, James, your father did agree to cover them and now they're looking for a doctor. I can't put them off. The man is absolutely insistent a doctor goes to the Airport immediately. He said it's very urgent."

"It'd have to be very urgent to get me to leave this crowd. I can't tell them I'm going off on a jaunt up to the airport in the middle of their vaccinations and I've no idea when I'll be back."

"It does seem important," Ida insisted. "By the sound of it the Captain on the aeroplane is in a panic. If you have to go, I'll explain everything to the patients. I'm sure they'll understand."

"Well then, what's the problem?" I sighed.

"There's a flight coming in from London and the Captain radioed ahead to say he has a child on board with a high temperature who's behaving strangely."

I laughed with relief.

"That's not serious, Ida," I said. "Children with a high temperature behave strangely because they're delirious. That's easy to deal with. All the Captain has to do it get the parents to give the child paracetamol and sponge him down with tepid water. If they're still worried about the child when they land, they can bring him here and I'll see him immediately. Why is the captain making such a fuss about a child with a temperature?"

Ida didn't say anything. That had to be another bad sign.

"I did suggest that to the Airport official but unfortunately it's not so simple." she said. "The little boy boarded the plane in London on a connecting flight from Africa. The captain is concerned he may be suffering from some tropical disease, particularly as the family are travelling from Northern Nigeria. Apparently there was a recent outbreak of Lassa fever in the area they've come from."

"Lassa fever," I exclaimed in alarm. "What do you mean, Lassa fever, Ida? You're not telling me they think the child has Lassa fever and they want me to diagnose it are you? I don't even know how to spell Lassa."

"James. I'm sorry," Ida said gently "but I'm afraid the Captain does want you to decide if the child has a serious illness or not and whether he can disembark his passengers. The official said you'll have to decide if the passengers need to go into quarantine or not."

Quarantine? Me decide? I was speechless. I knew virtually nothing about tropical diseases and even less about Lassa fever. I'd spent half an hour the night before my final examinations glancing over the short section on tropical diseases in my medical text book. I decided most of the diseases were too hard to spell and that it was highly unlikely I'd be asked to diagnose a case of schistosomsiasis from inner city Dublin in my finals.

I was alarmed at the massive responsibility that had suddenly been heaped on my shoulders. I didn't know what to do or who to turn to for help. What would happen if I went on to that plane with my extremely limited knowledge of tropical diseases and decided the child had Lassa fever? The child, the passengers, the crew and myself, would all be put into quarantine. If it turned out he didn't have the disease who would ever believe anything I said again?

On the other hand, if I gave the all clear and the child did have Lassa, what would happen then? I could see the headlines already,

'Doctor makes wrong diagnosis. Two hundred passengers let off airplane with Lassa fever due to Doctors stupid decision' or 'Doctor makes wrong diagnosis. Two hundred weary passengers kept needlessly in quarantine overnight due to Doctors stupid decision.' I couldn't win either way.

Today, the whole thing would be dealt with simply. I would contact the local health board and they would sort the matter out. Thirty five years ago, I felt very much on my own.

I left the surgery in Ida's hands and slipped out the back door to the car. As I drove grimly towards the airport I promised myself I would never ever do a G.P. locum again as long as I lived. There was too much of the unexpected to deal with. The only good thing about the call out was escaping those vaccinations. I told Ida to ask the mothers to come back in three month's. I figured my father would be back from holiday by then and I would have moved on to my next post.

In the 1970s security was tight in Northern Ireland because of The Troubles and especially at Government buildings and Airports. Ida said I was to go to the Airport police where I would be taken straight through security to the plane which was already on the tarmac. The thought of all those passengers already waiting for me made me feel weak at the knees.

I parked my car and approached the policeman on duty. He looked me up and down suspiciously and stared at the medical bag I was carrying.

"Where are you off to, mate?" he asked without taking his eyes off the bag.

"I'm Dr Griffin," I said "I was asked to see a patient on the flight from London."

"Is that right?" he said, still staring at my bag.

"I was told to go to the police station and they would take me on board the aeroplane to see a sick child."

He looked at me in disbelief. "You, see a sick child? You're not Doctor Griffin. I know him. He's an old boy with glasses."

"I'm his son. The Dr Griffin you know is on holiday."

I could see it was on the tip of his tongue to tell me I was too young to be a doctor. I was getting used to that. I looked about eighteen when I qualified but if there was any more of this stress, that would soon change. I dragged my driving licence out of my pocket and showed it to him. He looked at it and shouted into the adjoining room, "The Doc's here for the London plane, Sarge."

He nodded for me to follow him. I got the same incredulous look from the Sergeant, followed by a hurried whisper as he called the constable into his office. I could hear every word they said.

"Yes, I know he looks like a kid, Sarge but he has a positive I.D. I checked it myself."

"What sort of I.D.?"

"A driving licence."

"He looks too young to have a driving licence, Jack, never mind him being a doctor."

"Well, it says doctor on his driving licence, I checked it out. Come on, Sarge, we better let him through. They're in a complete panic on that plane."

The Sergeant came over and stared at me before telling me to follow him. We went out to the police car waiting on the tarmac. I clambered into the back seat between two burly policemen in flak jackets who were nursing sub machine guns on their knees. I clutched my case against my chest as we were driven at speed out to the plane that was isolated on the runway. It seemed to be in quarantine already.

The Captain was waiting anxiously at the bottom of the steps.

"Here's Dr Griffin, Captain Pickering," the Sergeant said with a smirk. "He'll be looking after this case for you."

I watched the Captain to see his reaction at having such a difficult problem dealt with by someone so young and inexperienced. Captain Pickering was too polite to let his feelings show. He was one of the old school types and didn't bat an eye-lid as he shook my hand.

"Thank you for coming so promptly, Dr Griffin," he said. "Would you be so kind as to follow me please?"

He turned and climbed up to the aeroplane. I followed him and nodded to the three air hostesses who were hovering at the top of the steps.

It was a hot day and the heat, stress and embarrassment had me perspiring to an uncomfortable degree. I could feel my clothes sticking to my skin and was acutely aware of my beaming red face. This was by far the most stressful and anxious moment of my life. I'd gone to my bedoom to look up Lassa Fever in my text book before driving to the airport but couldn't find the book - then I remembered I'd lent it to one of my brothers.

I knew nothing about the disease and still didn't even know if it was spelt with one or two S's. I would have preferred to take my finals over again in Greek rather than face this daunting task.

We stopped at the top of the steps. Captain Pickering explained that for the last two years, the child's family had been living twenty miles from an area in Northern Nigeria where Lassa fever had been reported.

"As I'm sure you're aware, Dr Griffin," he said, "Lassa fever is a highly contagious and frequently fatal disease. Somehow word got round the aeroplane when the child became ill that the family came from an area in Africa where Lassa fever is endemic. The news spread like wildfire among the passengers. I'm sure you'll appreciate it hasn't made things easy for myself and my crew trying to keep things calm. Some of the passengers are on the verge of becoming hysterical."

I was on the verge of having a panic attack myself and the Captain's words did nothing to reassure me.

As we walked down the aisle to the patient who was at the rear of the plane, I could feel the tension all around. Many of the passengers were returning from holidaying in Spain and had caught a connecting flight at Heathrow. They were sun tanned and dressed in bright clothes. Their heads turned as we made our way along the aisle. I could see the anxiety etched in their faces.

We paused to let a woman back into her seat and I heard a man mutter to his wife, "Would you look at the cut of him, Sally. He's meant to be a doctor and him hardly out of short trousers."

"He doesn't look like a doctor to me, Jimmy, he's far too young. I hope he knows what he's doing or we could all end up dead," she replied in a hysterically loud voice. An almost palpable wave of fear ran through the aircraft.

Captain Pickering stopped beside the woman and said firmly, "Excuse me, Madam. I must ask you to refrain from speaking in that manner. You are causing unnecessary alarm and frightening the other passengers. Dr Griffin is a fully qualified doctor. I have every confidence in him and I have no doubt he will make the correct diagnosis and get us all out of here safely. I would ask you in the meantime, to please control yourself."

I felt the last remaining shreds of courage ebb out of me as I dragged my feet like lumps of lead towards the back of the plane.

The patient was a ten year old boy called Patrick. He had been taken to the rear seat of the airplane. The two seats in front had been vacated and a curtain put up to give the family some degree of privacy and to create a small area of quarantine. The Captain stood outside and gave me a further briefing.

Patrick developed a temperature four hours after leaving Kano in Northen Nigeria. He hadn't been particularly unwell until shortly after his connecting plane had taken off from Heathrow en route for Belfast. He started complaining then of a sore head and throat and vomited twice. His mother noticed his face had become a little swollen.

When the parents mentioned his temperature and headache to a passenger sitting beside them and added that they were returning from Jos in Nigeria, the man became alarmed. He had worked in the tropics for twenty years and thought Patrick's symptoms could be the first signs of Lassa fever. Captain

Pickering stressed the man was not medically qualified though that hadn't prevented him from telling the parents that Lassa fever was a deadly disease which could kill within hours of contact. That really put the wind up everybody then.

My knowledge of Lassa fever had been enhanced by the information the Captain had just given me about it being a deadly disease found in Northern Nigeria that could kill within hours. That did nothing to increase my confidence or allay my anxiety about diagnosing the disease.

Captain Pickering pushed the curtain aside and walked in. I took a deep breath and followed. Patrick's parents looked up anxiously. Their expression darkened, was my age such a problem? My supposedly nonchalant mask was slipping rapidly.

"Mr and Mrs McKibben," he said, "May I introduce you to Dr Griffin who has come to examine Patrick and sort everything out." Captain Pickering stepped aside to let me past, then left. I was completely on my own.

"Hello, Mr and Mrs McKibben," I said in my best bed-side manner as I shook their hands. I noticed how cold and clammy my hand felt compared to theirs. I wondered briefly if I would get Lassa fever from shaking their hands and maybe die quickly, saving myself from any further humiliation. Mr and Mrs McKibben stared at me waiting for me to speak. I knew I had to get a grip on myself and say something to retain my professionalism.

"Ask the parents how Patrick is," a small voice prompted from the back of my mind.

"How is Patrick?" I blurted out.

'You've got to steady up,' I said to myself when I realized my voice had a nervous tremor. 'You've been in worse situations than this,' and the little voice inside my head replied, 'name one, just one.'

"He's not one bit well, not one bit well at all, Dr Griffin. We're very, very concerned about him" Mrs McKibben said sharply. She looked at me closely. I could almost read her thoughts.

"How can this young lad be a doctor. He looks far too young and will he know enough to diagnose what is wrong with our Patrick?"

"Are you not feeling well then, Patrick?" I asked, turning towards him. He was a sturdy looking little lad of ten with short black hair and brown eyes. His face looked pale and tired. It was a little swollen on one side.

"I'm not so bad thank you, Dr Griffin," Patrick replied with a smile. It was the first good thing I'd heard in the last hour. At least Patrick was polite and stoical and not a bad mannered little whinger. That was a big plus for me.

He was obviously tired but not desperately ill. That had to be a good sign too. Surely anyone with Lassa fever would be a lot worse than, 'not too bad.'

"You don't feel too bad then, Patrick? I said trying to look reassuringly at his parents. They didn't seem reassured. I continued. " Are you sore anywhere?"

"Well, only a little bit sore here" and he pointed to his swollen jaw.

"Come on, Patrick," his mother interrupted crossly, "what are you playing at? Half an hour ago, you told me your jaw was very sore and that you had a terrible headache and now you're telling the doctor you're not too bad. How can the doctor make a proper diagnosis if you keep changing your story. You have to tell Dr Grffin the truth if you want him to help you."

"I am telling the truth, Mum." Patrick said. "I think the medicine you gave me must be working, I feel a lot better. Maybe being so high up in the sky made me feel sicker. My headache's gone and my throat hardly hurts at all now."

I liked this little lad more and more. He was playing everything down. He couldn't have Lassa fever if Paracetamol on it's own made him feel a lot better. Could he? Paracetamol wouldn't have any effect on something as deadly as Lassa fever. It was only logical. .

'But what about trypanosomiasis, Leishmaniasis or Paracoccidiodomycosis?" a doubting little voice whispered in my ear. 'They're a lot harder to spell than Lassa and harder to diagnose. Could it maybe be one of those?' I mentally choked that little voice as I saw the first glimmer of hope.

It was beginning to look like I might get off this plane after all with my reputation intact though I still had Mr McKibben to deal with. He was standing for no nonsense from his son.

"Patrick," he said firmly, "you've been telling us for the past hour your head is splitting and your throat is aching. Why have you now decided to change your story?"

"Well, Dad, I haven't really changed my story. It's just that I don't feel too bad any more. I'm a lot better that I was, that's all. The headache's gone and my throat is just a tiny bit sore"

'Good man, yourself, Patrick,' I said to myself. 'Deny everything. Say there's nothing wrong with you. Tell them you've never felt better in your entire life and I'll be off this plane in a jiffy and five thousand miles north of the nearest case of Lassa fever.'

"Patrick," I said, "could you tell me what way you feel right this minute?"

"I'm just a bit tired, Doctor, that's all. We were up very early this morning and drove for miles and miles to get to the airport in Kano. I think that might be why I feel so tired."

"What time did you get up at this morning, Patrick?"

"One o'clock."

Things were looking up on all fronts - for me as well as for the patient ...feeling better, slight sore throat, no headache, tired after a long journey ....

I put a thermometer in his mouth for a full minute to give myself time to think. I needed to examine Patrick thoroughly and come up with a diagnosis. I was sure now he hadn't Lassa Fever but what was wrong with him? I needed a diagnosis for everybody's peace of mind.

His temperature was a little raised and his face was swollen and tender over the left side of his jaw. His chest and abdomen were normal. I looked at his ears, throat and mouth very carefully, hoping for some kind of inspiration. I noticed a small swelling inside his mouth on the left side of his jaw near an upper molar tooth.

"What's that? I asked myself. I had seen something like it before a long time ago but I just couldn't remember what it was or when I saw it.

Then it came to me.

"Has Patrick been in contact with mumps?" I asked his parents. I was barely able to contain my excitement.

"No. I don't think so," his mother said, shaking her head.

"Hold on a minute, Melanie," her husband said. "He was in contact with mumps if you think about it. It was a good while ago though. We were at a party in our Compound in Jos about three or four weeks ago and I heard a Scottish boy at the party developed mumps a couple of days later. But that was nearly a month ago. Surely that's too long ago for Patrick to have picked it up."

I felt a ton weight lift off my shoulders,

'Thank you Patrick. Thank you so much for making everything so straight forward in the end. You've got a dose of good old fashioned mumps - none of that nasty Lassa fever for you, my boy!' I wanted to shout out to all those doubting faces I'd passed in the aisle. 'Who's too young and inexperienced to sort this out then?' I had to stop myself punching the air in exuberation.

"Patrick has mumps." I said to Mr and Mrs McKibben, in as matter of fact a voice as I could muster. "It has an incubation time of eighteen to twenty one days and is only developing now after his contact with that Scottish boy three weeks ago. He has one-sided mumps, unilateral mumps it's called. About a third of the people who get mumps have a swelling above the jaw on one side only. That's what Patrick has. He isn't too bad at the moment and he's not likely to get any worse, so you can take him home. Keep giving him Paracetamol to ease the pain and to bring down his temperature. If his temperature doesn't come down with that, you'll have to sponge him with tepid water. He should be better in three or four days time."

I pointed out the typical mumps swelling on Patrick's face and the redness around Stensons duct in his mouth that confirmed the diagnosis. His parents were very relieved.

"Do you mind if I let Captain Pickering know that Patrick has mumps so the other passengers can be disembarked?"

"No, no. Not at all. Not at all, Dr Griffin and thank you very much for seeing Patrick and finding out what was wrong with him so quickly. We thought from what was being said that he had some dreadful, incurable, tropical disease," his mother said. There was no doubting the relief in her voice.

47

I savoured the moment as I stepped out from behind the curtain. I kept my face stoney as I beckoned to Captain Pickering. He walked rapidly up the aisle looking very worried. All the passengers stopped talking as he approached. They leant on the back of their seats and stared at me trying to guess what the outcome was going to be. They looked very, very apprehensive.

When Captain Pickering reached the back of the plane I looked at him very solemnly, "Captain, I have something to tell you," I said and paused for a couple of seconds. His eyebrows went up in alarm. "Captain, I have to tell you....."

"Yes, yes, what is it, Dr Griffin?" Captain Pickering looked as if he was about to collapse. I looked at him steadily without speaking, savouring the moment.

"It's safe," I said.

"Safe? What's safe?"

"It's safe. It's safe for everyone to disembark. There's no Lassa fever. Patrick has the mumps."

"The mumps," he gasped, "the mumps? Is that all? That's great news. That's great, really great. Good man, good man yourself, Dr Griffin and well done, Patrick."

Captain Pickering was one happy man. He couldn't have been happier if I'd appeared from behind the curtain and told him his wife had just delivered twins. As I walked down the aisle all the passengers began to applaud. One of the air hostesses gave me a beautiful smile and whispered, "Good work, Doctor, we knew you could do it." I felt ten feet tall.

On the way back from the runway my suspicious policeman friend was driving the car. He turned to me and said, "I hope you know what you're doing, letting all them people off that plane with a killer disease. If you don't mind me

48

saying, you don't look too experienced to me to diagnose a serious illness. I wouldn't want any of that Lassa fever in this country or any of them other queer tropical diseases either just because a young, inexperienced doctor like you doesn't know his job properly."

"I wouldn't blame you, Constable," I said, "I wouldn't want any of those deadly diseases in here either. Now you've made me not so sure if I got it right at all. I promise you one thing though, Constable."

"And what's that?" he snapped.

"If there is an outbreak of Lassa fever, I'll make sure you get the first vaccine that becomes available if and when it's ever discovered."

Airport 2

They say that lightning never strikes twice. It does.

Two days after the Lassa fever incident, I'd just shown my last patient out and was sitting back relaxing for a minute before getting myself a cup of coffee and a slice of fruit cake when Ida knocked on the door. When she came in I knew by the look on her face she had bad news.

"You're never going to believe this," she said with a nervous smile.

I looked at her and my heart sank.

"Go on, Ida, try me," I said. "I've seen that look before. I know something bad has happened. I suppose you're going to tell me I've got twelve home visits instead of four."

"No, worse than that, James, much worse."

"Much worse!" I almost shouted, "what do you mean much worse? There can't be anything worse than that."

I was feeling totally shattered. I had been out to an emergency in the middle of the night. When I got back I had fallen asleep after tossing and turning for an hour. Then I was called out again. On top of that, it had been a difficult surgery that ran on a lot longer than usual.

"It's the airport again." Ida said.

"The airport? I don't believe you, Ida. You're joking. You're pulling my leg. Please tell me you're joking."

"I wish I was but it is the airport. The Captain of an aeroplane about to land has developed chest pain. He wants a doctor at the airport to meet the plane."

"That's not my problem Ida," I said, "that's definitely not one for me. If anyone has chest pain, no matter who or where they are, they need an ambulance to take them straight to the nearest hospital. It can get to them a lot sooner than I can and has all the equipment for dealing with heart emergencies. They should have called an ambulance right away for a case like that. Put a call through to the centre and make sure they send one out immediately."

"I wish it was as simple as that," Ida replied, "but it isn't. There's a problem. The Captain insists he doesn't want to go to hospital. He wants to see a G.P. He said he'll explain everything to him when he sees him and not to anyone else."

"He needs an ambulance Ida – like everyone else with chest pain," I insisted.

"I'm sorry to disagree with you James, but the Airport official is adamant that the Captain is seen by a GP. He insists it's Company's policy as was explained to your father before he signed up. He got quite cross with me and said you were getting well enough paid for your trouble."

"Well enough paid, my eye." I exclaimed. "There's no money worth this amount of hassle."

Not for the first time I wished I'd stayed in the protected environment of hospital medicine where phone calls and patients had to go through a buffer zone of receptionists, nursing staff and junior interns before getting to me. Even then there was the option of calling in more senior staff to help out if the problem was too difficult for me to handle.

"Why doesn't that Captain get an ambulance like everybody else with chest pain. They're only too pleased to know an ambulance is on its way. They're usually complaining that it doesn't get to them quickly enough."

The thought of spending two or three hours at the airport sorting out a difficult problem and then getting back late for my home visits and evening surgery was too painful to

51

contemplate. On top of everything else, I was hungry after missing my breakfast. I hadn't even had time to eat that slice of fruit cake, never mind a cup of tea.

"I'm sorry, James," Ida said "but I think you'd better go. That official, for all his demands, sounded worried." I groaned as I threw my medical bag into the car and clambered in after it.

The first person I met at the airport was the policeman who had been on duty two days earlier.

"Hello, Doc, you again is it?" he greeted me, "I hope you'll not be making any more big blunders like the last time?"

"Did you ever get your Lassa vaccine sorted out, Constable?" I said as I followed the sergeant to the squad car.

The aeroplane had already landed and we sped across the tarmac towards it. I got out of the car and walked to the steps leading up to the plane. A tall, striking looking, no-nonsense air hostess who was obviously in charge was waiting for me.

"Are you the doctor?" she asked in a disapproving tone. She had obviously expected somebody else. She didn't seem to think much of the substitute.

I felt like saying, "No, I'm the assistant fish tank cleaner at Belfast Zoo," but I had already summed up that this was one lady who lacked a sense of humour. She might have believed me.

"Yes, I'm Dr Griffin," I told her. "Where is the man with the chest pain?"

"You'll see him soon enough," she said abruptly. "I think you ought to have a word with me first, Dr Griffin, before you see Captain McCrea. Captain McCrea is a young man and a headstrong one. He doesn't take advice from anyone and would have neglected his chest pain if I hadn't insisted he see a doctor."

I was delighted to hear he was young. That made it less likely that he'd taken a heart attack even if he had chest pain - but I could have done without the headstrong bit.

"We flew from Lanzarote to Belfast and Captain McCrea has been rubbing the centre of his chest for the last two hours of the flight. Quite frankly, I do not think Captain McCrea is in a fit state to fly this aircraft back to Lanzarote tonight, from a medical point of view, of course. He has been most uncooperative and absolutely refuses to go to hospital which was my first suggestion and has only agreed to see you under the greatest duress. I am sure you are aware that we have to follow protocol Dr Griffin. Captain McCrea has to be examined by a doctor to see if he is fit to fly. In my opinion he should be transferred to the nearest Emergency Department for a full cardiac assessment."

The Ice Maiden was trying to put pressure on me. If she had her way I would end up being piggy in the middle between her and her headstrong captain.

"Miss Carson," I said reading her name badge. "I'll need to examine Captain McCrea before I can come to any conclusions."

"Follow me then," she said sharply and marched up the steps of the plane to the cockpit door. She rapped loudly several times and ushered me inside without saying a word. When my eyes became accustomed to the darkness, I saw a small, red faced man staring at me angrily.

"What dae ye want?" he asked in a broad Scottish accent. "Was it ye who banged that door so noisily to annoy me?"

I was taken aback by his abruptness. "No, actually it wasn't, Captain McCrea. Miss Carson knocked on the door."

"That daft woman is always out to wind me up," he said crossly. "And she nearly always succeeds too. You'd think I'd

53

have learned by now. Who are ye and what dae ye want, anyway?"

"My name is Dr Griffin," I told him, "I've been asked to come and examine you."

"Not by me, ye haven't. It's that big, interfering Sassenach again. It's her that got you to come up here. If I had my way, I'd dump her in the middle of the Irish Sea."

Despite his belligerence, I felt there was something likeable about this little terrier of a man.

"I'm sorry you feel you're being pressurised into seeing me, Captain McCrea," I said. "If you prefer, I'll leave."

I cheered up at the thought of leaving under the guise of, 'patient refused medical attention'. The Airline Company couldn't complain about that.

"Well that wouldn't solve anything, would it? Madame Carson would report me for flying with chest pain and for refusing to see a doctor. There'd be all sorts of silly nonsense to go through for the next six months before we got it all sorted out. It wouldn't be worth it. I have to be examined by you whether I like it or not."

I didn't know what to say so I decided to follow my father's advice. "If you've nothing to say, say nothing."

Captain McCrea remained silent for the best part of a minute, "Look Doc, I've nothing against you and I'm sorry I was cross but it's not you I'm angry with. You're only doing your job. The fact is, I hurt some muscles in my chest yesterday morning mowing the lawn at home. The pain wasn't too bad until some brainless fool swung a heavy suitcase off a trolley and hit me full on the chest as we were going through the airport at Lanzarote this morning.

That silly woman Carson saw me rubbing my chest and took it into her thick skull I was having a heart attack and once she gets an idea into her head, it stays put. I tried to explain what happened but she wasn't listening. I'd have been as well talking to a haggis as talking to her. She's one of those women who are always right and listen to nobody.

He shook his head despondently and went silent again. "I know I've put you out getting you to come up here in the middle of your busy surgeries and I'm sorry for that but I had my reasons. I didn't want an ambulance called because there's nothing wrong with my heart. If I went to an emergency department, it would take hours for everything to be sorted out and we'd miss our slot to fly out of here. If that happened, we'd be above our time limit for the flight staff to be on duty and the flight would have to be postponed until tomorrow.

"The passengers would miss the first day of their holiday and the company would have to bear the cost of putting them up in a hotel overnight. That would cost thousands of pounds. I only moved to this airline a few weeks ago and I don't want to be costing them a fortune for nothing on one of my first flights abroad. I could end up losing my job. I have a young family and a mortgage to pay and, besides that, I know there's nothing wrong with me.

"All I need is for some sensible doctor to check me over and say I don't have a heart condition and that I'm fit to fly this aircraft back to Lanzarote."

I asked the Captain to come out to the main part of the plane where I could examine him properly. The Ice Maiden was waiting in the corridor with a, 'I told you so,' look on her face. I asked her to leave us in private. She gave me a cross look and reluctantly left.

I examined Captain McCrea. I listened to his chest and heart, checked his pulse and blood pressure and looked at his rib cage. I found everything to be normal except for a small area of bruising where the suitcase had knocked against his chest. I reassured him there was nothing wrong with his heart and, as far as I was concerned, he was perfectly fit to fly his aircraft back to Lanzarote.

He shook my hand and told me he would give me the freedom of Scotland for my help once he had the authority. I left him in the cockpit and walked down the steps where Miss Carson was waiting.

"Well Doctor?" she said, raising her eyebrows.

"Well, Miss Carson?" I replied.

"Are you going to tell me what's wrong with Captain McCrea?" she asked petulantly.

I felt like telling her it was none of her business and I didn't like her snotty nosed manner either. I bit my tongue and took a deep breath, "I'm sorry, Miss Carson, I can't give you any information about Captain McCrea, patient confidentiality you know. Perhaps if you asked him, he'll give you the details you require."

Miss Carson pulled herself up to her full height and looked at me furiously for several seconds before turning on her heel and stalking off.

I made my way back to my car and, once again, found myself face to face with the ubiquitous constable. He started straight away without stopping to take a breath.

"I hope you're not going to let that pilot with the heart attack fly his aeroplane out of here, not with all those people on board and the state he's in, are you?"

"I'm sorry, Constable, I'm not permitted to divulge that information, you know, patient confidentiality and all that. I'm sure the captain would have asked me to have a word with you if only he'd realized how concerned you were about his welfare."

I breathed a sigh of relief as I climbed into my car and drove home. I did have time after all for a sandwich and a cup of tea before doing my home visits.

Captain McCrea phoned me the following morning to say he felt much better after an uneventful trip to Lanzarote. Miss Carson had kept her mouth firmly shut the whole way back.

A Lesson Learnt

General Practice in Clonavon was a lot busier than I had imagined it would be. In my first two weeks I was called out three times to patients who had heart attacks at four o'clock in the morning, as well as to several other nightime emergencies. I saw two children with meningitis, six with bad measles and then there was Mrs Connolly's constipation to sort out as well as many other problems including those two stressful visits to the airport.

I was having a cup of tea with Ida one day and telling her about my experiences. She laughed. "You're having a time of it, aren't you James and all in your first two weeks? I've been working with your father for twenty years and in all that time he's never had as many problems as that in so short a time. Most of his work is humdrum, colds and coughs, bad backs, headaches and flu. Of course, there's always a chancer trying to get a sick certificate to stay off work, that sort of thing. He gets called to the odd farming accident and occasionally to someone with a heart attack or dying from cancer. That's about the height of any drama he has. On the whole, they're a healthy bunch around here and thank goodness emergencies are few and far between."

"The biggest emergency in his last few weeks was to old Mrs Murphy who fainted in the Chapel because of the heat and the length of the Canon's sermon. He was giving the Hellfire and Brimstone one and got carried away. If you stay around long enough, you'll find things flow along at a nice, steady pace."

I had my doubts but, as the weeks went by, I found that Ida was right. I'd find several people waiting outside when I opened the surgery at nine o'clock. If it was raining they waited in their cars or sheltered under the trees in the garden. I worked my way through them at a leisurely pace. The surgery doors were closed at eleven o'clock and I saw any patients who were still in the waiting room before I opened the post.

There was never much post then - two or three blood or urine results a week and an occasional hospital discharge letter. It was very different from today when a van calls at the surgery twice a day and collects a dozen or more blood and urine samples each time from the nurse. A couple of hours later, the results are e-mailed back.

It wasn't just so simple taking blood samples in the late 1960s and early 70s. I had no nurse and had to take all the samples myself, hand write the request forms and fill in the names and addresses of each patient on the sample bottles. (There were no electronically printed stick-on labels). The bottles had to be put in strong envelopes and rushed to the Post Office to catch the post and make sure they arrived in the Royal Victoria Hospital that day. The results were posted back two or three days later provided the bottles hadn't spilt or broken in transit. Nowadays an average post at Clonavon has sixty or seventy letters and blood results. Back then, I considered it a busy day if the postman brought more than five.

Once the post was sorted, it was time to make two or three home visits before lunch. I could then look forward to a quiet afternoon, that was until that tea break with Ida.

"Dr James," she said with her soft lilt, "you wouldn't by any chance be thinking of going to see Mrs Pringle on your rounds today would you?"

"Not really," I replied. I hadn't seen a call down for her in the home visit book but, when Ida looked at me and didn't say anything, I knew something was up. "Why, do you think I should go and see her?"

"Well, it's just that your father drops in on her every now and again to see how she's getting along. She's bed bound you know. I believe she's a lovely old lady and I'm sure she'd appreciate you calling in and so would her daughter who looks after her."

"I suppose if my father calls to see her regularly, I'd better do the same," I said with little enthusiasm. I had been hoping to nip into a book shop in Belfast after lunch to get a book that had rave reviews. There went my evening's reading in front of a cosy fire.

"I'm sorry to land that on you, James. I'm not trying to give you extra work. It's just that Mrs Pringle's daughter likes your father to call fairly regularly and make sure her mother isn't developing bed sores. The daughter seems to have a bit of a thing about bed sores."

"OK, Ida, I'll call today and while you're at it, are there any other housebound patients my father calls on regularly that I should know about?"

"Well, would you believe it, he does have one or two others he drops in to see fairly regularly?" and Ida gave one of her quiet smiles. "And as it just so happens I have a wee list right here in my pocket of his regulars."

She handed me a sheet of paper. I counted out fifty-six names.

"What!" I exclaimed, " you're not telling me he calls and sees all these people once a month are you, Ida? He'd never be at home at that rate."

"Your father's work can be quite steady actually James. Not busy as in busy, busy rushing around to urgent calls but it kept him going. He goes and sees some of these people twice a month or even more frequently. Mrs Pringle's daughter, Honoria for example likes him to drop in at least once a week and preferably twice. I think if she had her way she'd have him calling twice a day to check her mother out to make sure she doesn't develop those dreaded bedsores"

I sat looking the list feeling a little stunned. My workload had just been trebled. "What's Mrs McCarthy's name doing on this list, Ida?" I asked. "I saw her in the surgery yesterday morning. There wasn't too much wrong with her then. Why does she need a home visit when she's mobile and has her own transport and was able to make it to the surgery yesterday morning?"

"Yes, I know, James and didn't I get an earful from her about that. She came down to the surgery because she got herself into a state about her blood pressure. It hadn't been checked for four weeks since your father left. He generally calls in twice a month which keeps Mrs McCarthy happy."

"I bet it does. Where does he get the time to do that when he's going round seeing these other fifty-five patients as well?"

"Well, in the case of Mrs McCarthy, he generally goes and sees her on his half day. He calls in on his way back from shopping in Belfast with your mother. Mrs McCarthy loves to have a chat with your mother. She says she's a real lady and there aren't too many of them about. They have a cup of tea and a slice of Mrs McCarthy's date cake after your Dad has checked her blood pressure and given her the result. She writes it down in her little note book and compares it with the previous one, then she puts the kettle on. She's an awful nervous woman apparently.

"So that's what my parents have been doing for the last twenty years on their half day, having a cake and tea rave up with Mrs McCarthy? But can you explain one thing to me, Ida. If Mrs McCarthy is in such a bad way with her blood pressure, how did she manage to get herself down to the surgery yesterday morning."

Ida looked up to heaven. "Such a story I got about that," and Ida did a brief impression of an angry Mrs McCarthy wagging her finger.

"Fancy Dr Griffin leaving that young whippersnapper, Doctor James, to look after the likes of me with my nerves and my blood pressure while he goes off gallivanting round the world. You'd think he'd have more sense. I remember that James, when he was a wee boy in short trousers with a runny nose and to think he's now in charge of my blood pressure. It would put years on you if you thought about it. Did the doctor not tell him about my blood pressure? You'd think that's the least he could do what with him and his wife drinking tea in my house for the last twenty years."

Now that Ida mentioned it, I had a vague memory of my father saying something about a Mrs McCarthy and her blood pressure before he left but I'd forgotten he'd said she needed a home visit. He'd given me so many instructions before he went, he'd left my head spinning.

"You should have heard her going on about the young doctors of today and how lazy they are and how they don't care about anybody except themselves.

"Right, Ida," I interrupted, "I think I'm getting a message here that Mrs McCarthy was a very unhappy customer but could you just explain one thing to me, how did she get to the surgery yesterday if her blood pressure was meant to be so bad, which it wasn't?"

"Don't worry, James, I'm coming to that. I got every detail. Believe you me, she left nothing out. She had to phone her nephew who lives forty miles away in Dunloy. He had to take a morning off work and lose half a day's pay and got a ticking off from his boss into the bargain. The nephew was to pick her up at exactly a quarter past eight to make sure she was first in the queue at the surgery but he got a puncture and was late so she wasn't first in the queue. Mrs Moore, her lifelong enemy was. The two of them never got on since they were in the same class at school. Mrs Moore married the man Mrs McCarthy had her eye on"

"Hold on, hold on just a minute, Ida, why didn't she take the bus. There's one goes past her door every morning at eight o'clock. I passed it thousands of times on my way to school so I know that for a fact. If she'd taken that she could easily have been at the surgery by half past eight."

"Oh James, you don't know anything about the Mrs McCarthys of this world. Mrs McCarthy take a bus? It's out of the question. She'd sooner be seen in the back of a hearse. The shame of being seen in a bus and her a woman of means........"

"I thought she had three or four sons. Couldn't they have given her a lift?"

"I heard all about her sons too. Jim lives in England and does that young scamp of a doctor in yonder room expect him to come over every two weeks to bring his mother down to the surgery to have her blood pressure checked. Brian has emigrated to Canada, and John to Australia, and Harry is on holiday in Spain."

"OK, OK Ida." I said as I held my hands over my temples. "I think I'm receiving a strong message here and it's not telepathy. It's telling me it would be easier for everyone if I just called in and checked Mrs McCarthy's blood pressure every two weeks."

"That would be nice," Ida, smiled.

"And while I'm about it, are there any others like Mrs McCarthy on this list?" I asked "Sick but not sick, the worried well types?"

"Only about twenty," she said.

I sighed. No wonder my father had rarely been at home when I was growing up.

I sat staring at my empty coffee cup trying to take it all in. Ida waited for a minute before interrupting my thoughts.

"So you'll definitely be seeing Mrs Pringle this afternoon, James," she said.

The way she said it made me think there was something going on that I didn't know about. Had I been walking around in a dream world for the last few weeks since my father left? I began to wonder.

"Yes, I'll be there," I said, "but I've got this little strange feeling, Ida, that there's something more going on that I should maybe know about, a little behind the scenes scenario like Mrs McCarthy's?"

"Oh no, not at all," she replied. "Why, whatever put that idea into your head?"

"By the way you're going on. I'm getting a feeling I'm not seeing the big picture here. Go on, Ida, tell me. I can take it. Give it to me on the chin. Who was saying what about me and when?"

Ida gave a nervous laugh. "Well, now that you mention it and I don't want to upset you, James, I have heard one or two little whispers, so to speak, about the village. You know what it's like when there's any change in the village. It just so happened I was in McSweeny's shop this morning getting a bottle of milk when Molly Devine came in. Molly's a bit of a nosey parker and a busy body. As soon as she saw me she jerked her head back as if she'd just seen the devil himself. She started to speak in a loud voice for the benefit of everyone there.

"I suppose, Mr McSweeny, all them doctors are away on their holidays again enjoying themselves and leaving the likes of me and poor old Mrs Pringle to fend for ourselves. That poor old soul hasn't been out of her bed these ten long years but, sure, who cares about an old woman like her nowadays, certainly not the doctors. I can remember when Dr Hunter was alive, he never took a holiday, not once. He preferred to look after his patients. He'd never have left an old lady like Mrs Pringle without seeing her every week or every day if he had to.

I could see Molly's outburst had upset Ida. She was very loyal to my father and hated to hear anyone run him down.

"To tell you the truth, James, I felt like throwing my bag of sugar at her, the way she was going on in front of all those people about your father especially after all he has done for Mrs Pringle and that Devine woman over the years.

"So what did Mr McSweeny say?"

McSweeney was renowned for his tact. I wondered how he got out of that corner and kept everybody happy at the same time.

"Oh well now James," Ida said, "Mr McSweeney is a different kettle of fish altogether. He's a gentleman and knew how to handle that Devine woman. He had me in stitches the way he went on. He looked her straight in the face, "Well, Molly, do you know what I heard. I heard young Dr Griffin has been extra busy, powerful busy altogether these last few weeks. That's what I heard. He's hardly had a minute to get a bite to

65

eat, he's been that busy and him a young lad with a great appetite. I'll tell you something else I heard, Mrs Devine," he turned and winked at me. " I heard for what it's worth, not ten minutes ago and I do believe it was Barney the bread man who told me, Dr Griffin is going to visit Mrs Pringle this very afternoon. That's what I heard and that will be thirty two pence for your potatoes and two large turnips is it?" He carried on talking about the weather and how the winter nights were closing in and Christmas would be upon us before we knew what had hit us. Molly Devine spluttered and tried to have her say but couldn't get a word in edgeways no matter how hard she tried.

"I wanted to laugh so much I nearly left the shop without paying for my milk and sugar," and Ida started to laugh at the memory of Mrs Devine standing there with her mouth open and not getting a chance to speak.

When she stopped laughing, I asked her how Mr McSweeny and Barney the bread man could possibly know what I was going to be doing that afternoon before I did.

"Because, James," she said, "Mr McSweeny and Barney the breadman are two very wise men."

"OK, Ida." I said, "I see. I still have a bit to learn about this general practice business but I'm on this case anyway." I lifted my medical bag and went to see Mrs Pringle.

Mrs Pringle's Bed Sores

Mrs Pringle lived in a beautiful stone cottage on the outskirts of the village. It was surrounded by a well kept lawn. Tall copper beech and lime trees sheltered it from the weather. Her husband had been a colonel in the British army and had brought back colourful shrubs and plants from his travels abroad. He was a keen gardener and took pride in his exotic garden.

I often passed the cottage on my way home from school As a young boy, I would sometimes see the Colonel's two daughters playing a gentle game of tennis on a court marked out in the shade of the trees. The games stopped when Victoria, the younger daughter suddenly disappeared. It was rumoured in the village she was leading a bohemian life in Paris. Honoria was left looking after her ageing mother who was, by then, a widow.

I hadn't seen Mrs Pringle for almost twenty years. She never left her home. I remembered her as an elegant, refined lady who kept herself very much to herself.

I knew her daughter Honoria though only too well. We used to get the same bus into Belfast when I was a schoolboy. She taught Greek and Latin at a private school in the city.

Honoria rarely spoke to anyone at the bus stop. When she did, it was to tick off one of the boys in her clipped, educated accent. She was the first to arrive and was always there ten minutes before the bus was due. You could have set your watch by her. She was in her early thirties then, tall, neat and school marmish. Her face would have been handsome if it hadn't looked so severe.

When the bus arrived, she got on first. I was there before her once when I was up too early but I still didn't dare go in front of her. She always sat in the same seat. No-one considered taking it even when she was on holiday. She was the sort of person who could freeze you with a look. I was always glad I wasn't one of her pupils.

I wasn't relishing the prospect of renewing my acquaintance with Honoria although I was curious to meet her mother.

I walked up the gravel path to the door and knocked on the brass knocker. I could hear the sound echoing through the house and wished I hadn't knocked so hard. A few seconds later, a tall shadow appeared behind the frosted glass and the door swung silently open. Honoria stood in front of me.

I was shocked by the change in her. She had aged a lot. Her dark hair was almost white. She wasn't exactly untidy, more rumpled in her tweed skirt and brown blouse. Her face was lined with wrinkles that made her look sterner than ever. She still stood ram-rod straight.

I was given one of her disapproving looks, the sort you give to a dog who has just brought home something disagreeable.

"Yes," she said curtly. Honoria's manner hadn't changed. She always came straight to the point.

"Good afternoon, Miss Pringle," I said trying to sound more confident than I felt. "I'm Doctor Griffin. I've called to see your mother."

Why did she have to keep staring at me like that with her little bulldog eyes?

"I believe my father calls to see your mother. He asked me to come and see her while he's away."

I saw she was about to say something but changed her mind. Whatever she was intending to say would not have been, I was sure, very complimentary. Instead she opened the door a little wider, just wide enough for me to squeeze into the hallway.

"Please take a seat." It was an order not a request. "I will speak to mother." She disappeared up a long corridor almost at a gallop. I was a little shocked at her unbecoming behaviour. The Honoria I knew in the past would never have done that, bolting off like a disturbed donkey - she would have been too dignified. Age and stress can do strange things to us all.

I sat on the chair she had pointed to. It had a leopard skin draped over the back of it. The hall was dark and gloomy with wood panelling on the walls and mounted heads of water buffalo and antelope adorning every spare inch. They were obviously game the deceased colonel had shot. His twelve bore shot gun hung over a door just above a huge stuffed salmon in a glass case.

One wall was completely covered with black and white photographs. Most of them portrayed a well fed, portly gentleman grinning from ear to ear with one foot resting on a recently killed animal. He held the twelve bore proudly across his chest. I was leaning forward to get a better look when I heard Honoria racing back along the corridor. I straightened up immediately feeling like a little schoolboy again.

Honoria gave me another of her disapproving looks.

"Mother will see you now," she said before turning and marching down the dark corridor. I followed her at a half trot until we came to a closed door. Honoria swept it open and we came into a room of sunlight.

It was at the back of the house and not visible from the road. Everything was made of glass including the roof.

Delicate lace curtains covered the glass panels. I smelt the fragrance of roses from a vase of flowers on a bed-side table.

A frail old lady was propped up on several pillows with the whitest pillow cases I had ever seen. She gave me a beautiful smile and held out her hand for me to shake. I liked her immediately. How did a lovely woman like this rear a virago like Honoria I wondered as I shook her hand.

"Good afternoon, Dr Griffin. How nice of you to call and what a pleasure it is to see you." She sounded as if she meant it. "I remember you as a schoolboy getting the bus with Honoria. You've grown quite a bit since then."

I didn't know whether to be pleased or not. I glanced at Honoria. She certainly didn't look pleased. Small talk was not one of her strong points.

"Mother," she interrupted sharply, "you've been complaining for the last three days about a pain in your chest. I think you ought to tell the doctor about that."

Mrs Pringle gave a slight start when Honoria spoke. It was almost as if she was a little afraid of her. Mrs Pringle seemed weak. I noticed the small effort she made to talk left her slightly breathless. I wished Honoria would take herself off so I could have a chat with her mother and examine her without feeling that ominous presence hovering behind me. My prayers were answered when the phone rang in the hallway. Everything in the house was so silent, the ring of the phone sounded like a fog horn.

Honoria snorted angrily and, without a word, turned and left the room. She strode down the corridor to deal with the caller. I was glad I wasn't the one calling.

As soon as she left the room, Mrs Pringle beckoned me closer to her bed.

"Doctor, I've got to speak to you before Honoria comes back," she whispered as she grasped my hand. "You've got to get me in to hospital for a few days if you can. Honoria is completely exhausted looking after me though she won't admit it. I think she's on the verge of a breakdown and needs a long rest."

She turned and looked towards the door to make sure Honoria wasn't returning. There was little fear of that. Honoria was giving some unfortunate shop assistant a berating he'd never forget for not phoning when he'd promised. She sounded hysterical. Maybe her mother was right and Honoria was on the verge of a physical and mental breakdown.

"Now, doctor," Mrs Pringle continued, "Honoria will refuse to let me go to hospital. She will insist that I'll get bed sores and they'll get infected and I'll die. I'm a very old woman and if I do die, it's not the end of the world.

"I'm ruining Honoria's life keeping her here like this, looking after me. She won't let me go into a nursing home even though I've begged her time and time again. If you could even get me into hospital for a little rest I could maybe go into a convalescent home for a couple of weeks afterwards, I would......" She suddenly went quiet. Honoria had just given a roar of rage and slammed the phone down.

I could hear her grunting with exasperation as she sprinted back along the corridor. She came bursting into the room, her eyes almost bulging out of her head. I think she had forgotten I was there. She gave a little jump when she saw me and tried to compose herself. By the look on her face, I could see she had given one person a good telling off and was raring to give someone else a dose of the same medicine.

"I hope it's not going to be me," I thought as I opened my bag and took out a thermometer and my stethoscope. I examined Mrs Pringle slowly to give me time to think.

She had a temperature of 39 degrees C and signs and symptoms of pneumonia. I could probably have managed her at home and called twice a day until she was out of danger but, remembering her pleading, I decided to send her to hospital.

In those days, getting patients into hospital was straight forward. They were admitted directly to the wards by their G.P.s after he or she had spoken to the junior hospital doctor. Everyone did not have to be assessed in casualty like today. The hard bit was going to be breaking the news to Honoria.

"Well, Dr Griffin and how is mother?" Honoria snapped as I took the stethoscope from my ears.

"Actually, Miss Pringle," I said, "your mother is not as well as I had hoped." I chose my words carefully.

"What exactly do you mean by that?" She was almost snarling and had completely dropped her veneer of politeness. I could see the gloves were coming off. There was going to be no more Mr Nice guy.

"What I mean is that, em, your mother is, ah, not as, ah well as I had expected," I blabbered. I could feel my face flushing and a bead of perspiration forming on my brow as I braced myself for an interrogation.

"And what exactly does that mean, Dr Griffin. Mother not as well as you expected. Be precise." She was yelling now, her body hunched forward as if she was about to spring and grab me by the throat.

"Well, that means, ah, in precise terms, that means that your mother, ah, has pneumonia and has to go to hospital."

"What did you say?"

"I said your mother needs to go to hospital." There was a croaking quality to my voice I had never noticed before.

"That will not be happening," she said with finality. "That will most certainly not be happening. There is no question of my mother going to hospital," her voice was rising. I knew now how that shop assistant felt. "There is absolutely no question of that, she will not be going to hospital."

I didn't know what to say. I wished I was back in Kerry or Dublin or having a root canal filling - anywhere except in that room with that angry woman. She was working herself up into a fury. Her nostrils were flaring and she was breathing rapidly as she clenched and unclenched her fists. Honoria had become unstable with all the strain of looking after her mother for so many years. She was like a pressure cooker of rage that was about to explode. It seemed I was going to be the butt of all that anger and that didn't look like it was going to be a pleasant experience.

"Honnay, darling," a soft voice interrupted.

Honoria jerked her head round like a rattle snake about to strike.

"Honnay darling, it's me, Mumsie speaking my little darling. Don't upset yourself so. I want you to breathe nice and slowly now and just calm yourself down a teensy weensy little bit. Now listen to me for a moment like a good girl," Mrs Pringle spoke in such a soft, gentle voice, it would have slowed down a charging bull and it certainly slowed down her daughter's tirade. She reached forward and took hold of Honoria's hand and began to stroke it slowly and gently. "It's all for the best, Honnay darling. Everything's for the best. The doctor says I need to go to hospital and I feel myself that I should go there. So for my sake, darling, please listen to what the doctor advises and it will work out the best for everybody in the end."

Honoria seemed to have gone into a trance. Her features softened and her body slumped as she listened to her mother. After a few seconds she came to with a jerk and looked bewildered as she gazed around her. She made an effort to pull herself together but she looked like a beaten woman, her energy all gone. Her voice was resigned and full of fatigue.

"Alright mother, whatever you say. Dr Griffin will make the necessary arrangements."

I called an ambulance while Honoria collected the few things together her mother would need, Mrs Pringle called me over. She looked relieved and squeezed my hand.

"Thank you so much, Dr Griffin. You have no idea what a relief it is to me. You saw yourself the state Honoria's in. She's completely exhausted from looking after me but she won't admit it even to herself. She's too stubborn and full of that sense of duty her father instilled in her. She's got his pigheadedness too. She needs a long, long rest. Do you by any chance like W.B.Yeats poetry, doctor? He once wrote ' Too long a sacrifice can make a stone of the heart.' I'm afraid that's what's happening to my Honoria. It's such a dreadful pity and it's all my fault." She fell back on to her white pillow and shut her eyes. She was completely worn out.

As I wrote an admission letter, Honoria came back in with three sheets of paper in her hand. I could see her fighting spirit was back, I had to admire her. The woman was indomitable.

"These are my instructions for the management of Mother's skin and for her medication.," she said as she brusquely handed me the sheets of paper. "I have been looking after mother for twenty years and if these instructions are followed to the letter, she will not develop bed sores. You must

74

enclose them with your letter and order the nurses to carry them out each day exactly as I have written them."

I took the pages which were covered in small, precise handwriting.

One had a list of Mrs Pringle's medication giving exact details of when and how they were to be administered. As I glanced down the sheet, I had the feeling Honoria's instructions were going to be very unpopular with the nurses.

Slow K one tablet to be crushed and given with a spoonful of orange and lemon marmalade at 8.00a.m. and 8.00p.m.
Motilium, a quarter of an hour before breakfast – one tablet.
Iron tablets, one tablet twice a day with 20mls of cold water.
Largactil, one tablet with a cup of warm chocolate at bed time.
Fybogel sachet one twice a day in warm water with lemon juice to flavour

There were seventeen different tablets and medicines to be taken each day and some of them had to be taken two or three times a day. Each one had its own specific instructions.

I knew my father had cut her tablets down from twenty five a day to eight when he took her over as a patient after Honoria fell out with Doctor Hunter. That had not been popular with Honoria. She insisted on some new treatment every time he visited until the number of tablets had almost crept back to their original number. It is hard to stand your ground with someone as forceful as Honoria. No wonder Dr Hunter and my father had given in and written her up for what was mostly useless medication.

The second sheet of instructions was worse. It was Honoria's system for preventing the onset of bed sores. It included meticulous directions on how to massage susceptible areas several times a day with different oils and creams depending on the part of the body.

Heels – massage gently with warm olive oil four times a day and place on fresh cotton wool pad. Expose to air for two hours afterwards.

Elbows – apply Vaseline liberally twice daily.

There were six different areas to be attended to, each of them requiring different lotions at least twice a day.

The third page had more instructions on what food was necessary to help prevent bed sores, what temperature to keep the bedroom at and a reminder to check the room and Mrs Pringle's temperature three times a day. I wondered how Honoria had missed Mrs Pringle's temperature of 39 degrees C that morning. She was probably too stressed to notice it.

There was enough work on the three sheets to keep a nurse busy eighteen hours a day. I wondered how Honoria managed to remain sane for so long with the burden of work she had imposed on herself.

I enclosed the instructions with my letter thinking as I sealed the envelope that they would cause quite a stir on the ward. I could imagine Sister Robinson, who was prickly at the best of times, crumpling them up and throwing them into the nearest bin. My only regret was I wouldn't be there to see her explain that to Honoria. It would be like two dragons locking horns.

I shook Mrs Pringle's hand and Honoria showed me to the door. As we went down the dark corridor, I noticed a large propellor suspended from the ceiling of the dining room.

"Is that a real propeller?" I asked, my love of flying getting the better of me.

Honoria seemed pleased by my interest. Her face softened ever so slightly.

"Yes it is," she said. "Father shot that chap down in Flanders in 1916. He was trying to drop a large bomb on some of the men in my father's trench when he let him have it."

"Not with the twelve bore, I hope" I was tempted to say but thought the better of it.

When I called to see Mrs Pringle in hospital a few days later, I was accosted by Sister Robinson. She wasn't at all pleased with her patient's daughter or her sheets of instructions.

"Who does she think she is coming in here and trying to tell me how to run my ward? She has a list of orders the length of your arm about what I should be doing. The cheek of her! If I followed her silly instructions, I wouldn't have a single nurse free to deal with the other twenty-nine patients I have on this ward. Bed sores indeed! What's the country coming to with the patients and their relatives taking over the wards..." I let Sister Robinson rant on until she felt better and then muttered a few sympathetic words before going to see Mrs Pringle.

"How are you getting on?" I asked.

"I am getting on very well thank you, Dr Griffin and thank you so much for coming to see me. I really do appreciate all your help especially getting me into hospital." I could see talking was making her even more breathless than before as she continued. "I think Honoria is causing a bit of a commotion with the nurses with all her demands about looking after me

77

which I don't actually need. What can an old woman of eighty five expect from life. My time is up and, to tell you the truth, I'm not a bit sorry. Life has been a bit dull these last few years."

"Aren't you afraid of dying?" I asked.

Death and people's attitude to it interested me since the shock I got when I was eleven and saw a dead person for the first time. It was my Grandfather. He was a kindly man but in his coffin he looked cold and unfeeling. Where had all his warmth and goodness and sense of fun gone?

"Afraid of dying?" Mrs Pringle repeated. "I'm not in the slightest bit afraid. It's time for me to go. I know there's something far, far better ahead. I've had a good life and now it's time to leave. I believe this life is only a very small part of living and that real life begins after death." She paused to get her breath and smiled. "And do you know what I'm looking forward to most of all? It's seeing my husband, I can't wait to meet my silly stubborn Reginald again. I've missed him so terribly. I know he's waiting impatiently for me and he'll be so pleased to see me he'll forget all his years of military training. He'll break rank and run to me and throw his arms around me and hold me close to him forever and never let me go again."

Mrs Pringle stopped speaking and pulled a handkerchief from her sleeve to wipe away a tear. I waited while she composed herself.

"I'm sorry for being so emotional Dr Griffin," she said. "I'm sure you must think I'm just a silly old woman thinking like that about my husband at my age and talking such nonsense."

"No, no. Not at all, Mrs Pringle." I muttered. "It's not nonsense. It's not nonsense at all."

"That's very kind of you to say so, Dr Griffin." She took several deep breaths before continuing. "Do you know I've always loved poetry since I was a young girl, especially the romantic poets. Lord Byron wrote some awful rubbish but he had wonderful moments of brilliance too. 'Alas, the love of a woman. It is known to be a lovely and fearful thing.' He must have had old biddies like me in mind when he wrote that." Mrs Pringle's head flopped back on her pillow and she didn't speak for a minute. "I really don't know what's come over me. I suppose the strain of the last few months is beginning to affect me." She dabbed her eyes before going on in her quiet cultured voice.

"To answer your question, I'm feeling a lot better. The nurses and doctors couldn't be nicer or kinder. My only concern is Honoria. I know she won't accept my death even though it will be a great relief to her which is something she'll never admit. She'll blame herself and everyone else but there's nothing more anyone could have done. I don't know what will become of her. If it wasn't for that I'd be so happy to be at the end of my long journey. I'll just have to trust in Providence." Her head fell back on the pillow. She was exhausted. I pressed her hand gently and left.

Two days later, in the middle of morning surgery Ida knocked loudly on my door. When I went to see what was wrong, she said Honoria was on the phone demanding to speak to me immediately.

"She sounds very angry, James, very, very, very angry."

I didn't like the sound of that. Honoria was difficult enough to deal with when she wasn't angry.

"Could you tell her I'll phone back in ten minutes when I've finished with this patient."

"James, the way Honoria sounds, if I asked her to wait ten minutes, I think she'd run up here, rip your heart out with her bare hands and burn the surgery down."

"Does she sound that bad?" I was beginning to get the same uncomfortable feeling I got when I broke a window at school and was told the headmaster wanted to see me in his office immediately and that and he looked very, very angry.

"You'd better just have a word with her," Ida said softly.

I went to the phone like a condemned man. "Hello, good morning Miss...." I started in as breezy a tone as I could muster. Before I could say another word, Honoria exploded.

"Don't you good morning me you stupid man. How dare you good morning me after what has happened to mother."

She was the angriest person I had ever spoken to. She sounded as though she was about to flip her lid.

"Why? What has happened to your mother?" I stammered.

"She has bed sores, you fool. That's what's the matter. SHE HAS BED SORES. Can you understand that? After all my years of looking after her at home, feeding her, changing her and stopping her getting bed sores, you send her to hospital against my wishes. She's there for less than two weeks and she gets bed sores because those incompetent, stupid nurses, who are nearly as incompetent and stupid as you, neglect her. I'll make you pay for this, young man, if it's the last thing I do. You'll be struck off by the time I finish with you. You have ruined my life. It's completely ruined. The only thing I have to look forward to is bed sores and more bed sores. I can't stand it. I just can't stand it. And it's all your fault."

The line went silent for several seconds. I thought she had put the phone down. Then I heard a gurgling noise followed by wailing. Honoria was crying, sobbing uncontrollably. I tried to speak to her but the line went dead.

I phoned the hospital immediately and spoke to Sister Robinson. She sounded almost as cross as Honoria. I was having a bad day with angry women.

"That mad witch of a woman," Sister Robinson started, "is driving me round the bend with all her fussing about her mother and her bed sores. It seems to be the most important thing in the world to her. She never gives over about them. That's all she ever talks about from morning to night, bed sores, bed sores, bed sores. She comes in here or phones ten times a day to check up on us.

Yes, Mrs Pringle has a bed sore, the tiniest bed sore you can possible imagine. You have to search for it to find it. What do you expect in her condition? She's lost a lot of weight and eats and drinks next to nothing. She says she feels sick if she takes anything. What can we do to prevent bed sores in someone who is a bag of bones. It's impossible. I know her daughter says she wouldn't have got them at home but when she was at home, she wasn't as sick and breathless as she is now. We can't even turn her anymore without causing her a great deal of distress. Her daughter's talking about turning her every two hours like she does at home but that would kill her now. She's not fit for that any more. It would be too painful and, in any case, we haven't got the staff to do it.

On top of that, the old dear just wants to die quietly. She's told me herself several times. She doesn't want to go back to that crazy daughter of hers who'll turn her every thirty minutes and slap a bucketful of cream on her ten times a day. Mrs Pringle doesn't want any more of that. She just wants to die peacefully and with dignity."

Sister Robinson was one angry woman. If she'd been any crosser, steam would have come out of the phone. I commiserated with her and hung up.

I phoned Honoria back to explain her mother was deteriorating but was getting the best treatment the hospital could provide. She was a lot calmer but sounded totally broken down and dejected. After all her devoted care over the years without a break, the prospect of having to look after bed sores on top of everything else was just too much for even someone as tough as Honoria to handle.

Mrs Pringle died two days later from pneumonia. In the end, it was a relief for the poor woman. Honoria was grief stricken. I called at the house the following day to offer my condolences. Honoria was out making arrangements for the funeral but Mrs Pringle's other daughter, Victoria was there. I vaguely remembered her from my boyhood days as being a good-looking young woman who was always laughing. She used to play tennis effortlessly on their front lawn while, in contrast, Honoria lumbered around, shouting at the top of her voice every time she lost a point.

"Hello, Dr Griffin," she said with a smile, "I'm Vicky, Honoria's sister."

She was an elegant woman in her early forties. Her dark hair was swept back and fastened with a silver clasp that matched her ear rings. A Hermes scarf was draped carefully over a well cut black suit and white silk blouse. Combined with her twinkling blue eyes and poise, it made her look quite striking. As I shook her hand I thought this woman must have broken a lot of hearts in her day. She made me a cup of coffee and sat down in the sitting room opposite me. She had Honoria's cultivated voice but it was much softer.

"I'm so sorry I couldn't get back to see Mama before she died," she said, "my husband and I were staying in an isolated spot in Nepal and I only heard about her condition a few days ago. I had such a job getting back to Paris and then here."

Unlike her sister, Vicky liked to chat. In a few minutes she had given me a brief outline of her life, the family history and her concern for Honoria.

"Mama got quite a bad stoke twenty years ago. I had planned to go to Paris as an au pair but I cancelled that and stayed at home with Honoria to look after her instead. Mama begged us to let her go into a Nursing Home and to get on with our own lives. We wouldn't hear of it, especially after she had been so good to us all our lives. I looked after her for three years and at the end of that time, I felt worn out and depressed. It looked as though life was going to pass me by. Mama pleaded with me to go to Paris and enjoy my life and not to waste my youth. She said the same to Honoria over and over again but Honoria was having none of it. In the end I did leave. I felt terribly guilty about it and still do but I knew I couldn't stand the life I was leading any longer. It was breaking me down both mentally and physically doing the same work over and over again and never having a holiday or getting out even to the pictures. I felt as if I was on the verge of a nervous breakdown. Honoria was a bit of a stickler for doing your duty and never complaining – but I didn't have her enormous inner strength and stoicism.

"Honoria was very cross with me for leaving and that didn't help much either. I still don't know what the right answer was in the circumstance I found myself in but I just knew I couldn't go on with the life I was leading for a moment longer. It was one of those no win situations – stay and crack up or get out and feel guilty for the rest of your life. In the end I left. Mama was delighted when I told her I was going. She said that even though she would miss me terribly, she would be a lot happier knowing I was getting on with my life. She was a wonderful woman," Vicky said as she began to cry. She took out a handkerchief and dabbed her eyes before continuing.

"When I came home over the years, I could see how looking after Mama was affecting Honoria. She was getting crosser and crosser and harder to deal with. Everything had to be done her way. Mama was even a little afraid of her and was sometimes scared to speak in case it upset Honoria. I felt terrible leaving after each visit but I couldn't have coped, I didn't want to end up like Honoria who was destroying herself with all this extra work she was making for herself.

I felt dreadful at leaving all the burden on her but she completely refused to have any discussion about Mama going into a Nursing home and that was that.

The mistake we made was looking after Mama for too long at home through a misplaced sense of duty. She would have been better looked after in a Nursing Home being looked after by professional nursing staff. We would all have been happier. In the end, I just had to get out and so did Honoria but she refused. I think now that, unfortunately, she has nearly left it too late.

While we were talking Honoria suddenly arrived home. She was ashen faced. I felt an immediate tension in the room between the two sisters and thought it would be intrusive of me to remain. I made my excuses and left.

Vicky went back to Paris. A few months later, Honoria boarded up the house and left for a teaching post in Nairobi. A long time after, I heard she had given up that job and gone to work in a safari park looking after, of all things, Water Buffalo. Maybe she was trying to make up for all the ones her father had shot.

The neatly trimmed hedges soon became overgrown and weeds proliferated on the once manicured lawns. Over the years, slates fell off the roof and the window frames began to rot. Sometimes, when I drove past, I got a feeling of nostalgia for a time that was lost for ever as I remembered two young women in long flowing dresses playing tennis under the shade of green billowing lime trees.

Huggy Bear

Jack MacNamara was a hard man to pin down. He either wouldn't or couldn't give a straight answer to anything he was asked – and he didn't try too hard either.

"Hello Jack. It's a lovely day, isn't it?" I said to him one sunny afternoon. I was cutting the lawn and had stopped to empty the grass when I saw him passing slowly by on his black bicycle. He dismounted and eyed me suspiciously for several moments. I'd heard Jack could be an awkward individual and began to wonder if he would answer me at all.

"What makes you think it's such a great day, young lad? I've seen better," he said in a gruff voice. He looked me up and down as though suspecting me of wanting to steal his wallet or trick him into saying something spontaneous.

"Ah, I just thought what with the sun shining and the birds chirping, it was a lovely day," I said, wishing I hadn't spoken.

"I don't know that I'd agree with you on that point either. Anyway, I've better things to be doing with my time than wasting it talking about the weather," he said abruptly as he clambered onto his bike and lumbered into the middle of the road. I watched his tall gaunt figure disappear into the distance.

"And it was nice talking to you too, Mr Chatterbox," I muttered as I went back to cutting the grass.

I mentioned him to Bella the following morning when we were having a cup of coffee.

"Ah Jack MacNamara, sure I know him extra well, James – one awkward man is our Jack," she said "He's known the length and breadth of the country for his stubbornness and lack of humour. They use an old Ulster Scots word to describe him – brawn. That means beyond stubborn. The boys in the village nicknamed him 'Huggy Bear.' They seem to think that suits him even better than Brawn Jack."

A week later Jack turned up at the surgery complaining of pains in his stomach – at least that's what I eventually concluded though I was by no means sure. He gave the vaguest answers to my questions and seemed to resent being asked anything at all. It was on the tip of my tongue to tell him I had to ask questions because I didn't do telepathy but I don't think that would have pleased him either. Getting information from Huggy Bear was like extracting blood from a turnip.

As the ten minute consultation stretched into twenty minutes, I was still none the wiser about why Jack had come to the surgery, I asked a routine question about the functioning of his bowels.

"Why do you want to know that for? That's very personal and none of your business. My bowels indeed! A vet wouldn't ask a heifer that question. Confine yourself to medical matters. I'm here about my illness and ailments and not to be asked things like that that are of no concern of yours or of anybody else except myself."

I tried to explain it was a routine medical question but I might as well have explained the rules of synchronized swimming to a gerbil for all the interest he had in what I said.

Every question I asked was answered with a question or no answer at all or an answer that made no sense. After an exasperating twenty-five minutes, I'd had enough and decided just to write him out a prescription for some pain killers I'd recently been asked to try by a drug Rep. The tablets had tasted absolutely foul and smelt even worse. I thought they might do Jack some good but at worst they'd do him no harm.

I handed him the prescription.

"What's that for?" he asked distrustfully.

"That's for you," I couldn't resist saying. I'd had enough of his obtuse answers and decided it was time to give him back some of his own medicine.

"I know it's for me but what is it?" he sounded cross.

"It's a prescription."

"I know it's a prescription but what have you written on it?"

'Big strong words, a recipe for beetroot cake, something for yourself' flashed through my mind as possible responses but I didn't say them. I knew they wouldn't be well received. "I have written you a prescription for mephitic analgesia," I said.

"For what?"

"Mephitic analgesia."

"And what's that for?"

"That's for you."

"I know it's for me," he snapped "but what will it do for me?"

"It will make you better."

"How do you know it will it make me better?"

"Because it's mephitic analgesia"

"And what do those words – Mefic's Aunt mean?"

"By Mephitic Analgesia I mean I am prescribing you an anodyne, a palliative remedy. Mephitic Analgesia is something that will settle your symptoms."

"What symptoms?"

"The symptoms you told me about," I said, or to be truthful, I thought 'the symptoms I couldn't manage to drag out of you because you haven't answered one single question or spoken a word of sense since you came in here today and it's harder to get information out of you than extract an impacted molar from an angry, constipated buffalo.'

"Are you sure this stuff will help me?" There was that note of distrust again in his voice.

"Yes, it will." I said emphatically.

"How do you know it will?"

"Because you'll feel better when you take it."

"And how do you know I'll feel better?"

"Because you'll get better."

"How do you know that?"

"Because I've prescribed it before to people with your complaint and they've got better."

"How do you know they got better?"

"Because they told me."

"They told you," he said in disbelief. "When did they tell you?"

"The day after I gave them it."

"They told you the day after you gave them it?" I could see Huggy Bear didn't believe one word of that.

"Yes."

"How many of them told you?"

"All of them."

"All of them told you the next day?"

"Yes, every single one." I said distorting the truth slightly.

"I don't believe you."

"It's hard to believe, isn't it?"

"Very hard and I don't believe it either." Jack snorted to emphasise his disbelief. "And will this Mefics Aunt rubbish help me?"

"Yes, it will."

"How will I know?"

"Because you'll get better when you take it." It was like the Spanish Inquisition version of Twenty Questions.

"Do any other doctors use this stuff?"

89

"Yes, lots of doctors use it."

"You're not the only one are you because I don't trust young doctors with their new fangled ideas, experimenting on me."

"It is used by doctors in every country of the world."

"I don't believe a word of that. Who else uses it or recommends it besides you and that da of yours?" He was surly now.

"I'll tell you who uses it and recommends it and maybe you'll believe me then Mr MacNamara. It's used and recommended by physicians, surgeons, paediatricians, general practitioners, obstetricians, opthalmologists and otolaryngologists, The British Medical Association, the General Medical Council, the Medical Protection Society, the Medical Defense Union, the New England Journal of Medicine, The American Medical Association, the Lancet, the British Medical Journal, the Irish Medical Times ……" Huggy tried to interrupt but I wouldn't let him. He'd said too much already. It was my turn to speak and I was determined to keep spouting out all the weighty names I could think of until he stopped questioning me or was satisfied or left.

"… the Association of Australian and New Zealand Physicians, the Royal College of Surgeons of London, Ireland, Glasgow, Edinburgh and Alaska, the Royal …"

"Alright. Alright, alright. There's no need to go on and on," he roared. "I'll take it but I'll be back when I find out it's as useless as any of the treatment your da's ever given me."

"It's also recommended by the Royal College of Physicians of Ireland and London, GP magazine Pulse and Doctor, MIMS, the Australian Association ….."

He slammed the door as he stalked out. I sighed with relief and poured myself a glass of water before calling in the next patient. Talking nonsense can be very dehydrating.

Mrs O'Brien came into the surgery. She was a large lady who wore an overcoat and scarf, no matter what the weather. She was a woman who spoke her mind.

"Huggy Bear sure took his time getting sorted out and then after all that went off in a temper. What did you do to upset the poor man, Doctor?" she said as she sat down.

"I'm sorry, Mrs O'Brien but some consultations are more complicated than others and do take more time.

"Well Huggy's consultation must have been very, very complicated. It took that long, I thought he was moving in. But it's typical of that brawn man. Nothing's ever straightforward with him. You should have ejector seats for boys like that. Once they go two minutes over their time, give them a verbal warning and then press the red button. Straight into orbit for the likes of Huggy Bear is what I say." Mrs O'Brien was getting into her stride. If she kept going on at that rate it would be the red button treatment for her before she even got to her complaint.

"And how are you keeping yourself anyway, Mrs O'Brien?" I said trying to interrupt.

"Do you see that MacNamara man, Dr Griffin?" Mrs O'Brien wasn't going to be interrupted. "He was born ignorant and he'll die ignorant. He's as crooked as they come, the most awkward, difficult, sulky, fussy, over sensitive man ever to come out of Clonavon bar none, apart from that Ismael Maddon of course. Maddon's all of the above with knobs on and as cross as two bags of weasels into the bargain."

"Mrs O'Brien, if …." I tried to speak.

91

"I don't know how Huggy's wife puts up with him and the sulks he gets into if he thinks anyone has upset him and believe you me, it's not hard to upset the same man. She's a saint that woman, putting up with his nonsense. And do you see when Huggy falls out with you, well there are no half measures with our Huggy Bear – no indeed, no half measures at all. You're talking about the real deal when Huggy Bear huffs – the full blown fall out, the full works, the tenth degree treatment. He doesn't talk to you, your husband or wife, your brothers or sisters, your parents, aunts and uncles and all your living relations as far back as three generations – all your people and connections in fact. In a community like Clonavon that's a lot of people to have on your sulk list. If it wasn't for the fact he's the handiest man in Clonavon at fixing things, I don't think anybody would bother with him. He can fix anything if he's not sulking, from a washing machine to a diesel engine to a dog's broken paw and the fence that broke the paw. It's a pity he can't fix his bad moods."

"Mrs O'Brien, Mrs O'Brien, Mrs O'Brien." I had to shout to get her to listen. I tried to sound jocular. "You're sitting on my new ejector seat and I'm going to have to give you a verbal warning."

"What are you talking about Dr Griffin, a verbal warning?" She sounded shocked.

My little joke had gone down like a lead balloon.

"I mean, I mean …." I stammered trying to think of what to say.

"Oh you mean that sort of a verbal warning, the ejector seat verbal warning. " The penny had dropped. Mrs O'Brien smiled and then started to chuckle. When Mrs O'Brien chuckled, she really chuckled. She gave it the full works. She threw her head back and her fat cheeks and her two chins wobbled like big jellies. Her face went red and her shoulders shook. Tears came to her eyes and ran down her face. She snorted and gasped for breath at the same time. She laughed so long she became breathless and I began to worry she was taking an asthma attack.

She eventually managed to bring herself under control.

"You'd better hit that red button Dr Griffin right now, for I'm well over my time." That set her off into another paroxysm. She pulled herself to her feet still laughing and struggled to the door.

"What about your complaint, Mrs O'Brien?" I asked.

"My complaint? I've no complaint. Whatever it was is gone. Huggy Bear's been sulking with me for five years and that moan about him and the laugh I had was better than any tonic. I'd better leave before you send me into orbit on that newly installed seat of your." She laughed again as she staggered to the waiting room. I could hear her still laughing as she rolled down the avenue.

It's true what they say, some people make you feel better when they come and others when they go.

The Return of Huggy Bear

If everyone was like Mrs O'Brien I'd have had very little work. She came to the surgery with a complaint and went home cured and I hadn't done a single thing except listen to her. It reminded me of a situation when I was a junior doctor and the exact opposite happened.

I was working in a Dublin hospital when a man came to outpatients with nothing wrong with him and left with a litany of complaints.

I was assigned then to a cardiologist called Dr Aloysius Moriarity Brandon Brennan. Dr Brennan was, to put it mildly, eccentric. He said and did things I wouldn't have thought possible for a professional man or any man for that matter to say or do. He was the daftest, funniest, most volatile, brilliant, impatient and unpredictable man I ever met. He ran through his ward round and saw more patients than all the other consultants in his unit put together. He stormed through the hospital corridors at a half trot.

Dr Brennan arrived to do his outpatients clinics like a whirlwind every Monday and Wednesday afternoon. Three cubicles were reserved for him to examine his patients. He moved from one to the other so quickly that the nurses in each cubicle could barely keep up with him. He saw forty to fifty patients at every clinic without a break. He didn't believe in coffee breaks or his housemen having them either.

Each patient was brought to his desk by a nurse and asked to sit down in front of Dr Brennan as he rapidly read their notes. He was able to scan several pages in a matter of seconds and draw out the essentials. He'd fire out one or two questions to the patients and if there was the slightest hesitation in their

94

replies, he'd point to a cubicle. "Cubicle one, Student Nurse Fox" and he'd call for the next patient to be brought forward. He knew everybody's name including all the porters and auxillaries and the medical and nursing students which was very flattering but also part of his 'method.' It kept everyone on their toes.

Three patients were seated in a line four or five yards from his desk to make sure there were never any hold ups in the flow. As soon as Student Nurse Fox led her patient to his cubicle, a patient from the line was brought forward and set in front of Dr Brennan. My job was to note down what investigations or treatment he wanted for each patient. It was extremely demanding keeping up with his rapid fire instructions.

When Dr Brennan went into a cubicle he quickly examined the heart and chest as he called out notes to myself or his other houseman. The nurses were instructed to have the appropriate areas to be examined exposed, so there were no delays with patients undressing.

One afternoon a man of forty was called forward to the desk.

"How long have you had chest pain, Mr Collins?" Dr Brennan asked, glancing up from his notes.

"I haven't got chest pain. I'm here ..."

Dr Brennan immediately interrupted as he impatiently tapped the doctors referral letter. "Your GP Dr Murtagh has clearly stated you have chest pain. Nurse O'Callaghan. Cubicle two for Mr Collins please." Dr Brennan had little time for people who didn't know if they had chest pain or not.

Mr Collins tried to object as he was dragged to his feet by Nurse O'Callaghan.

Nurse O'Callaghan was a sturdy country girl who took no nonsense from anybody. She pulled the protesting Mr Collins towards Cubicle two. She knew only too well how cross Dr Brennan would be if she hadn't her patient prepared by the time he got to her. As far as she was concerned, whether Mr Collins liked it or not, Dr Brennan was going to have no reason to be cross with her.

Two minutes later Dr Brennan stormed into the cubicle almost ripping the curtains off their rails in his haste.

I was following at a half gallop and was amazed to see Mr Collins sitting on the examining couch with his arms folded across his chest and a stubborn look on his face. What was more astonishing was that he still had his shirt on and looked like he had no intention of removing it for his examination despite Nurse O'Callaghan's best efforts.

"What's the meaning of this Mr Collins?" Dr Brennan spluttered. He had gone from being benignly irascible to volcanic eruption rage in a split second. I could see gallons of blood flooding into his face through bulging veins in his neck. His eyes looked as if they were about to pop out of his head. Dr Brennan didn't deal well with delays.

"I don't need to be examined Dr Brennan. I'm ….."

"You don't need to be examined?" Dr Brennan repeated in an angry whisper. He was so cross he could hardly speak. "Since when did you start making decisions about who needs to be examined and who doesn't, Mr Collins? Do you think I can divine what is wrong with your heart by just looking at you or diagnose the Aortic Stenosis your doctor has picked up from his examination which, incidentally I might add, is a grade three murmur. Just remind me when you qualified as a doctor and trained as a cardiologist Mr Collins? Nurse O'Callaghan please open Mr Collins shirt in the way you have been instructed without any further delay. Refusing to be examined indeed. What next? I suppose you'll be looking to take over my job."

Mr Collins was so taken aback by Dr Brennan's onslaught, his arms slumped to his side. Two of his shirt buttons were quickly opened and Dr Brennan plonked his stethoscope over his heart. He moved it around for several seconds listening intently.

"That's strange," he muttered to himself. "I don't hear any murmurs. Dr Mutagh has never made a mistake like this before." He listened again and shook his head. "Definitely no murmurs there. As normal a heart as I've ever heard. What was going through Murtaghs head?"

Mr Collins had recovered his composure and was determined to speak.

"There are a couple of things I need to point out to you Dr Brennan and please show me the courtesy of listening. First of all, I am NOT Mr Collins. Second of all, there is nothing wrong with my heart as you have just said. Finally, I am the taxi driver who brought Mr Collins to hospital for his outpatients appointment with you. He is waiting outside in my taxi. I came in here to borrow a wheelchair. Mr Collins gets breathless when he walks."

There was a stunned silence as the man who was not Mr Collins eyeballed Dr Brennan.

Dr Brennan went from volcanic red to a deathly pallor in a matter of seconds. He cleared his throat several times. "Nurse O'Callaghan, could you please get this gentleman a wheelchair?" he gulped before turning and marching straight into the next cubicle.

We all had a laugh about what we called 'Brennan's Blunder' – everybody, that is, except Dr Brennan who never mentioned it again. One thing about Dr Brennan though, life was never dull when he was around.

When I had been in Clonavon two months, I made a similar blunder myself or a 'Griffin Goof-up' as I called it.

One evening I opened the surgery door hoping it wouldn't be busy. I wanted to get into Belfast to do some Christmas shopping.

Other people must have had the same idea. There was only one patient in the waiting room. I was delighted until the patient looked up from his newspaper and I saw it was Huggy Bear MacNamara.

He stood up when he saw me and gave me a cold stare. Without saying a word he marched into the consulting room and sat down. I took a deep breath and followed.

"Well, Mr MacNamara. How are you getting on?" I asked. I knew better than to make any casual observations about the weather.

"I don't know what way I am," he said.

"You don't know what way you are?" I repeated. What sort of an answer was that? If he doesn't know what way he is, how could he expect me to know what way he was?

"Yes, I don't know what way I am," he said emphatically.

My heart sank.

This was going to be worse than his last visit.

"When you say you don't know what way you are Mr MacNamara, could you explain what you mean by that?" I asked. I didn't expect to get a sensible answer and I wasn't disappointed.

"When I say I don't know what way I am, I mean what I say which is I don't know what way I am." Huggy Bear looked at me with a cross face that made him look like a very cross, huffy bear whose porridge had just been stolen. He was obviously not on for any form of cross examination.

"Right, right. That's fine. That's OK Mr MacNamara." I said trying to placate him. "I think I know what you mean. When you say you don't know what way you are, I think what you're saying is you're not well? Isn't that what you mean?"

"That is not what I mean. For your information I am neither well nor sick," he answered.

"So that's why you said you don't know what way you are?" He nodded his head the way you do when someone you think is a bit slow on the uptake, comes up with an answer that has been staring them in the face for a very long time. I was ten minutes into the consultation and none the wiser why Jack MacNamara had come to see me.

"Is there any way you could maybe expand on that a bit, Mr MacNamara, you know, sort of give me an idea of what exactly not knowing what way you are means and at the same time being neither sick nor well," I said hesitantly.

"Not knowing what way I am and being neither sick nor well is plain everyday language. I can't put it any plainer or explain it any better. It says exactly what I mean and means exactly what I say. You doctors should be able to understand plain talk after all them years of book learning and dissecting dead frogs and human beings and educated high falutin' talk you've been doing at them Colleges you go to. Maybe if you weren't drinking so much of your whiskey and wine and beer and playing less of your cricket and hurling and football and enjoying yourselves so much on the tax payers money, you'd understand better what the plain people of Ireland mean when they speak in their own everyday language."

Jack glared at me and tugged his black cloth cap over his forehead to show his displeasure. I got the feeling he didn't like students enjoying themselves, especially medical students.

'Ok,' I thought, 'time to approach this from a different angle.'

"Ah, I see what you mean now. In other words what you're saying is that you're not right."

"I'm right enough," Jack said dourly.

"But maybe not as right as you were say last week" I suggested.

"I wouldn't agree with that line of talk either. I'm neither right or not right and for your information I was rightly last week."

I could see what was coming next.

"In fact," he continued "as I've just said, I don't know what way I am."

"Ok, Jack. To summarize and to get things clear in my own mind, what you're saying is you're right but at the same time not right, you're neither sick nor well and you don't know what way you are." I had difficulty keeping the sarcasm out of my voice.

"That about sums it up, doc." Jack said. "You seem to be catching on. There's hope for you yet in this doctoring game." He pulled his cap back off this forehead to show his approval.

"Thank you Jack," I mumbled. "That's very kind of you and so encouraging as well."

At the same time I was thinking how could I get this long winded man to talk sense and find out what was wrong with him.

"Ok, Jack. I'm going to have to get a little bit technical in my line of questioning here."

His face clouded over. "Is that so?" he said and pulled his cap down again, hiding half his face. "I don't like the sound of that, too interfering and nosey by the sounds of it."

"Oh no Jack, there'll be no interfering questions or nosey ones either, just technical ones which are very different."

"What way different to nosey ones?" he demanded.

"Less personal and less nosey," I blabbered. He really was an awkward customer. Bella was wrong. Brawn wasn't a strong enough word to describe Jack. Donkey obstinate would be a better description – though it insulted donkeys.

"I don't know if I like the sound of that."

"It's Ok, Jack, you'll find the questions easy enough and no problem once you get into them."

He looked at me crossly and said nothing. In a situation like this where I was being given half baked answers to every question I asked and each answer worse then the next, I needed to go through a routine medical question checklist of all the body systems to rule out any serious diseases. I'd start at his head and work my way down to his feet though leaving the bowels out. I knew Jack didn't like personal questions but there was no other way for me to proceed if I was to get any information out of him and make a diagnosis. Otherwise I wouldn't be able to get him out of my surgery before Christmas, never mind getting any Christmas shopping done.

"Have you had any headaches recently, Mr MacNamara?"

"Why would I have headaches?" Jack snapped, "I've never had a headache in my life. I've told you I don't know what way I am. What's that to do with headaches?"

"I'll take that as a no then, Mr MacNamara." I sighed.

"You can take it whatever way you like."

The routine medical questions looked like they were going to be non starters.

"Have you a pain anywhere?" I knew as soon as I asked it was the wrong question.

"Of course I've pain. Who doesn't have pain at my age? Name me one man of seventy-two years of age in the whole of Ireland, North and South of the border who doesn't have pain. Every bit of me is in pain and why wouldn't it be at my age? What sort of an eejit question is that?"

I groaned. At this rate the consultation was going to take forever.

"I'm sorry Mr MacNamara but that's what's called a routine medical question. Part of my training during my seven years of Medical studies was learning to ask routine questions like the one I've just asked you."

"I don't care what big name it's called or how many years you studied that sort of nonsense, I don't like it either way. And what do you ask those interfering questions for anyway? They're more like nosey questions to me."

Jack looked like an enraged bull. Some patients never cease to amaze me with their expectations. Did Jack think I was some sort of a mystic who could divine what was wrong with him just by looking at him? I wondered what sort of questions he expected doctors to ask him if they weren't to be personal – maybe quiz him on the internal workings of a combustion engine or how his grandfather clock worked or ask about the milk quota of his neighbours cows.

"Look Mr MacNamara," I said. "I'm at a bit of a loss as to how to continue if you feel you can't answer the questions I've been medically trained to ask. It would be negligent of me if I didn't."

"I can answer any questions you ask but them ones you're asking are just plain daft. You must take me for some sort of a fool." Jack pulled his cap lower over his head. I could hardly see his face.

"I'm sorry about that. That wasn't my intention, Mr MacNamara, I'll try something different that I hope won't upset you." I didn't want Jack sinking into one of his black huffs. Life is hard enough without one of your patients putting your name in their sulk book.

"I need to get some idea of how long you've been feeling the way you are – you know, the way you explained how you don't know what way you are." I was being as gentle as I could.

"I've been like that for a while," he said in a huffy voice.

"A while Jack," I repeated.

"That's what I said, a while." Jack was digging his heels in.

"When you say a while, would that be a week, two weeks or maybe a bit less or a little bit more?"

"When I say a while, I mean a while," he said crossly.

I hesitated before going on. It seemed futile and Jack was getting angrier by the minute. At the same time I had a 'duty of care'. Doctors have a responsibility to make a reasonable effort to find out what is wrong with a patient even when the patient is not reasonable. The best example is a patient with mental illness who might be unreasonable, unco-operative and even violent. A doctor still has a duty of care for those patients. Despite his personal feelings, fears or prejudices, a doctor must take every reasonable step he can to find out what is wrong with his patient.

"Would a while be counted in days or hours, Mr MacNamara?" I asked tentatively.

"A while is a while and no more and no less," he snapped.

"Would three months be considered a while then?"

Huggy pulled his cap back and stared at me as if I was the greatest fool he'd ever met. "That would be a good while, not a while."

I realized I was going nowhere with my questions and only wasting my time.

"Ok, Ok then, Mr MacNamara, that's fine. I'll leave it at that," I said. "I won't put you through any more questions. I can see you're upset. We'll just move onto the examination."

This consultation was moving towards vetinary medicine where the diagnosis is made by examining rather than by asking questions. I hoped when I examined Huggy Bear I'd get some idea of what was wrong – a sore throat or possibly an ear or chest infection or maybe a fast heart.

"They'll be nobody examining me." Jack said emphatically. "They'll be nobody laying so much as a finger on my person, never mind laying any form of an instrument near me." Jack made it clear there was going to be no further discussion about that. He sat fuming with his arms folded tightly across his chest and looking straight ahead.

"You don't seem happy Mr MacNamara," I ventured.

"You're dead right I'm not happy. I'm not one bit happy about your line of interrogation or any of your eejit talk about putting me through an examination."

"Could you please tell me why you're not happy about either of those?"

"I'll tell you why I'm not happy. I told the wife a good half hour ago to hold my dinner back because I was coming around here for what I thought was a two minutes chat. And now you've kept me the best part of forty minutes with your questions and wanting to examine me."

"But that's because you said you weren't well, Mr MacNamara. It's my job to ask people who aren't well questions and to examine them if necessary."

"I never said I wasn't well. I said I didn't know what way I was but that's not saying I wasn't well."

"But you told me a few minutes ago that you were neither well not sick."

"And what about it?" he snapped.

"As far as my understanding goes, that means you're not completely well."

"Where I come from it means I'm rightly."

"Rightly?"

"Aye, rightly." Jack looked really cross. There was no point arguing with him.

I felt as exasperated as he did and I still had no idea what he was talking about. A line from one of Harry Belafonte's songs came to mind. "It was as clear as mud but it covered the ground."

'That about sums this up' I thought as Jack ranted on.

"I came round to this waiting room tonight because nobody answered your front door when I rang the bell. I only called in to the waiting room after that to say I've fixed your da's wheelbarrow and I wanted to know where to put it and are you going to pay me now or have I to wait until he comes back. And the next thing I knows, you starts up this rigmarole about me not being well and a whole line of interfering questions that are nobody's business but my own."

It was incredible. After all that time wasting, he'd just come to find out where to put my father's wheelbarrow!.

I took the barrow and paid in cash. He nodded curtly and left. He wasn't exactly whistling but at least he was happier.

After he'd gone I leant back and put my feet on the desk. To tell you the truth I didn't know what way I was. I was neither sick nor well, right or not right and I was like that for a while - and a good while at that until I felt rightly.

The Canon

As far as I knew, Canon Creen had never had a day's illness in his life. He was one of the most respected man in Clonavon. Some people said he was a saint, others thought differently. Whatever he was, he was a hard man to ignore. As soon as he came into a room, you were aware of his presence.

When I returned to be my fathers locum, Canon Creen had been the parish priest of Clonavon for forty years. He had always impressed me when I was an altar boy by his fairness – but also by his strictness. When I came home as a doctor, I still had a great fondness for him but at the same time a lot of respect.

The Canon was a craggy, sinewy man. Even when he was old, he looked distinguished although his tall frame had begun to stoop.

He always wore a black cassock and a biretta, legacies of his time as a student in Rome. His cassocks were so old they had a green haze about the elbow and down the front. The only time I ever saw him walk slowly was when he read his breviary. If the weather was fine, he read it as he strolled beneath the pine trees in his garden, holding the black book at arm's length.

He strode everywhere, the tails of his cassock flying out behind him and came into a room like a whirlwind. He set off on his daily three mile walk at a half trot.

He kept himself fit all his life and surprised my mother one day when he turned eighty by holding out his hand straight in front of him and kicking his foot up to touch it.

"How's that for an old man?" he said

When I was doing my home visits I often saw him striding along the road on his daily walk. One afternoon I noticed he was walking slower than usual and wondered if age had finally caught up with him. I drove past him a few days later and he was limping.

"Are you all right there, Canon?" I called out of the window as I slowed down.

"Right as rain James, right as rain. And how's yourself?" he replied as he struggled to walk normally.

"You seem to have a bit of a limp there, Canon," I said.

"What limp are you talking about young lad? I don't see any limp." I saw the effort of trying not to limp bring beads of perspiration to his brow.

"Well Canon, let me know if that limp ever comes back and I'll have a look at your foot," I said

"Any limp I had is gone," he said with a cheery grin, "thanks all the same."

I drove off and, looking in the mirror, saw him revert to his hobbling gait when he thought I was out of sight. "What's that old man up to?" I wondered.

A week later, I saw him outside the parochial house walking slowly and using a walking stick. I stopped the car.

"That limp seems to be back again, Canon." I said

He looked at me with doleful eyes.

"Well I suppose it is but that's life, James. Arthritis, I'd say and at my age no surprise - only to be expected. God granted me eighty years of perfect health and I have a lot to be thankful for."

I could see he was upset and trying to put a brave face on it. He'd told me once that his daily walk was one of the greatest gifts of his life. "It keeps me trim and fit and gives me the appetite of a ploughman. It clears my head of any worries and puts me in a reflective mood. As I walk I look at the four seasons of the year and the changing beauty of the world and marvel at God's hand in nature.

All that joy and pleasure looked like it had suddenly been taken from him. No wonder he was downcast. His sparkling eyes were listless and dull. Even a holy man finds God's will hard to stomach at times.

"It's a little cross for me to bear James, just a little cross that's all. I'll offer the loss of it up for the Holy Souls. And what did you think of Celtic last weekend?" he said trying to change the subject. He never liked to complain or talk about himself. I was impressed by his lack of self pity.

"If you don't mind, Canon," I said, ignoring his question, "I'd like to have a look at your foot. I might be able to do something for you."

His eyes lit up for a second at the hope of any help. "I don't think there's anything you can do James. You can't reverse the clock."

"I'll have a look anyway, if you don't mind." I insisted.

"Well, that would be kind of you," he said as he sat on the grass bank and threw his walking stick beside him. He started unlacing his old worn out hob-nailed boot carefully. When he had the lace undone, he eased his foot slowly from the boot, grimacing in pain all the time. I saw the tip of his sock was stuck to the end of his big toe and matted with blood and pus.

"Can you take your sock off too Canon?" I asked when he made no effort to remove it.

"Taking that sock off nearly kills me, James. It's too painful. The sock is stuck to the toe. I slept with it on the last three nights. The last time I took it off I had to soak the foot in warm water for half an hour. Even the slightest knock against the toe is like someone sticking a knife into me. That's why I had to take the boot off so slowly."

"I'm sorry Canon but the sock will have to come off if I'm to examine you properly. I can help you with it if you like. I've a simple procedure for taking off socks," I said as I thought 'There'll be no half hour soakings to take that sock off.'

"Have you?" he said as he looked at me with his big, blue, innocent eyes full of trust.

"I have indeed, Canon," I hated myself for saying it but in the end it was going to save the Canon a lot of pain and both of us a lot of time.

I gently pulled the sock down to his ankle and then taking one side in each hand I yanked it off. As it came over the big toe I felt some resistance and gave it an extra tug. The effect on the Canon was electrifying.

He leapt into the air with a roar. For a second or two I thought he was going to say something that wasn't biblical. He lurched forward and caught my arms in a vice like grip as he howled in anger and pain. I was relieved he hadn't grabbed me by the throat. I knew he was struggling to say something worthy of a Canon. It was a moment when goodness was vying with evil.

He took an enormous breath and let it out very slowly.

"You got the sock off alright, James," he croaked, "but it wasn't exactly what I had in mind."

"No pain, no gain, Canon," I said a little glibly as I rubbed my arms and examined his big toe.

"I have good news for you Canon," I said with a grin. He looked up in disbelief as he tried to get his enormously red swollen toe to move.

"Is that so, James? I find that hard to believe in the circumstances."

"I can cure your toe and have you back walking in three days time," I said.

"That's impossible James. It would take a miracle to do that."

"Look at the miraculous speed I got your sock off. You wouldn't have believed that was possible. I can't cure the toe just as quickly but I can do something to settle it down."

"What can you do?" he asked ignoring my remark about the sock miracle.

"You have an ingrowing toenail Canon that has become infected. That's why your toe is so red and swollen and full of pus. I can take out the bit of nail that's sticking into you and causing all the problem. That redness and swelling around the toe will go away once the ingrown nail is removed."

"And how do you propose to do that?" he asked suspiciously.

"A minor procedure is all that's needed. A very minor procedure," I said trying to sound reassuring. I knew I had a bit of ground to make up after the sock incident.

"I thought taking the sock off was supposed to be a minor procedure. It was the most painful experience of my life."

"This will be a lot easier Canon." I explained how I would numb his toe with an injection and cut out the offending piece of nail.

"And when would you propose to do that?"

"Right this minute if you're agreeable. I can guarantee you'll be pain free in half an hour. Now if you'd like, you can get into the car as you are and I'll take you down to the surgery and we'll get everything sorted. You can leave the sock off for the moment," I added with a grin.

We drove to the surgery and I injected local anesthetic into the base of his toe on both sides, creating what is called a ring

111

block (i.e. numbing all of the toe). Five minutes later I handed him the jagged piece of nail that had been sticking into him and causing so much pain.

"Is that the little lad that caused me all that bother?" he asked in amazement.

"That's it Canon, that's all it was, a little bit of nail growing in the wrong place."

"Are you sure that's all that's wrong with me – an ingrown toenail?"

"That's it, that's all that was wrong with you."

"Thank God for that," he said with a lot of feeling. "To tell you the truth, James, I was worried. I thought I was finished. I thought I'd taken the gout like my grandfather. He got gout in his big toe when he was sixty seven and it swelled up as big as a bap. It looked awful, red and painful, just like my toe. It killed him in the end after a lot of suffering. The gout went through him and into his kidneys. The pain was so bad, at times he couldn't bear to have a sheet on top of his toe even in the middle of a freezing winter. When it was at its worst, we weren't allowed to go into his bedroom. The vibrations of our feet on the wooden floor put him into such agony. I thought that's what I'd in store for me and I wasn't relishing the thought of it at all." He sighed with relief.

"Your toe is fixed, Canon. You won't have any more bother with it. There's little chance of you getting gout at your age anyway and even if you did, you'd never be as bad as your grandfather. There's very good treatment for gout nowadays not like in your grandfather's time. Still it's a bit unusual to see an ingrown toenail for the first time in someone of your age. It's a condition you usually get in your teens if you're going to get it at all. You must have done something to damage your nail in the last few months to bring it on," I said.

112

"Now that you mention it, I dropped a concrete block onto my foot five or six months ago when I was building a bit of a wall in my back garden. I wouldn't recommend it, dropping the block on your toe I mean. The block broke the nail in two but I thought it settled down okay after a week or two. It wasn't anything as bad though as the pain of the ingrown nail when I knocked it against anything."

"I'd keep away from concrete blocks if I were you Canon, especially where dropping them on your foot is concerned. Anyway, that's what caused all the trouble," I said. "Your toe's cured now. If you've any further bother with it, I'll take the foot off." I looked at him seriously for a moment. He became so alarmed I started to laugh.

"Just one of my little jokes, Canon," I said as I showed him to the door.

Three days later I saw him striding past Chapel Hill as though he hadn't a care in the world.

The Canon was a contradiction. In many ways he was humble yet he had a great reverence for the dignity of his own priesthood.

"It's not me that is important," he'd say, "it's what I represent and that is Christ, the Creator of the Universe."

He was both complex and simple. He was interested in everything that went on in the parish. He was as fascinated by the number of bales of hay that Mick Heaney got from his back field or who had scored the goals in the boys' football match as he was in the structure of a DNA molecule or the inner workings of the Second Vatican Council. When he looked at you he gave you his undivided attention. It could be a bit unnerving but flattering at the same time.

113

He was one of thirteen children, born at a time when religious bigotry was rampant in Ireland. His father was a Protestant and his mother a Catholic. His father often said the day he met Mary Molloy from Dunloy, he knew she was the woman for him. Despite objections from both families, they married and never let their different religions come between them. The children were brought up Catholics and the father went to his son's ordination and received his first blessing. Despite that he remained a Protestant all his life.

Because of his upbringing, the Canon was ahead of his time in ecumenism. He didn't like any form of bigotry. In the 1940s and 50s the landed gentry were almost entirely Protestant. When they went hunting in Clonavon, he invited them into the Parochial House for a drink before they set off.

I remember as a boy seeing men and women in red jackets riding up his avenue and the hounds racing round the garden, whimpering, and fretful to be off. It was part of country life in those days.

Despite his ecumenical views, he was a fanatical Glasgow Celtic supporter and was gloomy for days when they lost. He went to Parkhead with one of his parishioners who was almost as fanatical as he was, three or four times a year.

He was a classical scholar and met frequently with Rev. George Turnbull who was the Church of Ireland rector and a graduate of Trinity College, Dublin. The two of them got on really well. They'd stroll along speaking a language that nobody understood.

The Canon enjoyed my father's company. I often saw the two of them deep in conversation, almost always talking about religion. He talked to my father as a man would talk to his son. I remember him getting a little cross with my father once and that was when he asked the Canon to explain The Holy Trinity.

"Even if I could explain The Holy Trinity to you, Paddy, you wouldn't understand it. I only understand the slightest fraction myself and that's after years of studying it. It's an immensely complicated subject of infinite dimensions that the greatest saints couldn't even begin to grasp – and you're like myself Paddy, no saint or at best a little saint in the making. Anyway, God will explain all of it to you Himself if you're that interested but in His own time and that's when you're dead. You'll have to be patient 'til then, Paddy. Don't be fretting yourself or me by asking any more about it in the meantime."

My father was happy with the Canon's explanation and that was the end of the matter.

If my father was going off for one of his rare days away from the practice, he'd sometimes ask the Canon along. That annoyed my mother. It wasn't that she didn't like the Canon but she loved to have a day out with my father all to herself and away from the family. There weren't many opportunities for that with the busy lives they led but going to Dublin for the Christmas shopping was one of them. My father could never understand her just wanting to be with him when there was the chance the Canon could come along too. (He didn't understand a lot when it suited him).

"We'll have great fun with the Canon. He can tell us stories about his time abroad and the interesting people he's met in his life and the great books he's read."

"I'd rather talk to you about Sara's schoolwork or Brian's eczema and buying Thomas a new pair of football boots," she'd insist.

"Sure we can talk to the Canon about all that. He has a powerful interest in that sort of thing."

They'd set off to Dublin with the Canon sitting in the front seat beside my father and all the talk would be about some esoteric aspect of religion which my father had picked up on when he was at one of his meetings of the Third Order of Mount Carmel. There was never a word mentioned about Brian's eczema or Thomas's football boots.

My mother would sit in the back seething with irritation at my father's lack of understanding. She'd cheer up however, once they were a few miles down the road at the prospect of a day's shopping. On one occasion, even that didn't lift her mood. When my father took a corner too fast and made her slide across the back seat (pre seat belt days), she shouted out, "Are you trying to kill us all, you fool?"

The Canon looked at my father with a twinkle in his eye.

"I see now why you bring me with you to Dublin, Paddy, - self protection." My mother shook her head. Two men – one stupider than the next. They understood nothing.

My father and the Canon often exchanged books on religion and occasionally my father got me to leave one in the Parochial House. I loved those occasions even though they scared me.

The Parochial House was an imposing, nineteenth century building with expansive lawns. Three stone steps lead to the front porch. The garden was dominated by a huge, monkey puzzle tree, the only one in Clonavon. I often thought of climbing it but didn't dare. The aura of the Canon and the shadow of the big house banished any idea of that.

The Canon was usually in his room when I called. I'd ring the huge brass door bell and listen to the sound of it echoing down the long corridor. I seemed to wait there for a long time but I suppose it was only a minute before old Mrs McNulty would emerge from the kitchen wearing a starched white apron. She didn't like time wasters taking up the Canon's time.

Once when Mrs McNulty took longer than usual to answer the door, I rang the bell a second time thinking she hadn't heard it, I kept my finger on the buzzer for a good ten seconds. There was a roar of irritation followed by hurried foot steps. The front door was almost pulled off its hinges as the Canon ripped it open. He stood in the doorway wearing only his trousers and a string vest. His face was covered with shaving cream. I had obviously caught him at a bad time.

"What do you think you're doing, ringing the bell like that, you young brat," he bellowed. "If you ever do that again, your father will hear about it."

I was so shocked by the way he was dressed I couldn't speak. I'd only ever seen him in clerical garb and presumed he slept in his cassock. I was once surprised to see a pair of striped pyjamas hanging on the line and wondered who owned them. I never rang the doorbell twice again.

If Mrs McNulty decided I had a genuine reason for seeing the Canon, she'd lead me along the gloomy wood panelled, corridor to his study. She'd knock twice and wait. I'd hear paper rustling and, sometimes, a deep sigh.

"Yes, who is it?" his stentorian voice would boom out.

"It's Dr Griffin's boy Canon Creen with a book he says his father has sent."

"Enter," he'd shout.

Mrs McNulty would quietly open the door and nod for me to go in. I'd shuffle in and stand waiting for the Canon to speak. Children knew not to speak until he addressed them.

"You're James, Dr Griffin's boy, aren't you?" he'd say fixing his eyes on me.

"Yes, Canon Creen."

"You have a book for me."

"Yes Canon."

He'd stretch out his hand and I'd give him the book. He'd take it without saying a word. Then came the bit I liked best – the Canon's reaction. He'd glance at the title and the first page. If it didn't interest him, he'd fling it on to his big black sofa with a snort of irritation and say he'd read it later. I knew he'd never look at it because it would still be in the same position on the sofa the next time I called.

If he liked the title and the first page, he'd start reading it straight away with a ferocious intensity. He wouldn't even sit down. It was as if he had become part of the book. He'd completely forget I was there. After a few minutes when Mrs McNulty didn't hear any voices, she would cautiously open the door and beckon me. I'd slip out and be off home without him noticing. But if he tossed the book aside, he'd call Mrs McNulty and she'd appear almost immediately standing just outside the door while he gave his instructions.

"Get the boy some lemonade and biscuits, Mrs McNulty," he'd order and I'd be taken down the dark corridor and made to sit at the biggest table I'd ever seen while Mrs McNulty fetched the lemonade.

My father always knew if the Canon didn't like his book by the red rim round my lips from the lemonade.

Occasionally when I went round on one of my book trips, the Canon would be sitting in the shade of a tree. One day he was in great spirits when I came across him. He was obviously enjoying the book he had on his lap.

"I've a great little book here," he said. "It's in French and its about the roots of Greek verbs. It will help me read Homer."

I didn't know what he was talking about but I tried to look interested. I went home and told my father the Canon was reading a book about the roots of Greek trees written by a Frenchman. I can remember my father thinking it was an odd thing to interest him. It was only years later when I saw the same book on someone's coffee table that the penny dropped.

I was an altar boy with him for seven years. He was strict and wouldn't tolerate any form of horseplay in the chapel especially before Mass. Every midnight Mass at Christmas, he thanked the altar boys from the pulpit in a way that made us glow with pride and later on he'd give us a box of chocolates, an unheard of gift in those days.

The Canon had a serious side to his character but also a very light side "God first and fun after" was his motto. He loved to laugh and laugh a lot. He took a lot of time teaching us the words of O'Rafferty's pig. When we sang it he roared with laughter from start to finish. I can still remember the words although it's a long time since I sang them.

'O'Rafferty's pig had a big pot-belly
Though built like a battleship, solid and stout.
When he walked he wobbled like a jelly
Impudence written all over his snout.

With God always in his mind, the Canon had no fear about frightening his parishioners if he thought it was good for their immortal souls. "Better to be scared in this life and prepared for the next" was one of his often repeated mantras.

His Hell Fire and Brimstone sermons could be heard the length and breadth of Clonavon and were discussed for weeks after. They cast terror into everyone especially when he quoted with great authority, the visions that some of the saints had of hell. The attendance at confession always went up for a week after those sermons.

He liked complete silence when he spoke in Church. If anyone had the audacity to cough, he'd stare at them and shout,

"Will you do me the courtesy of controlling your barking. You sound like a walrus."

Occasionally when I went to Chapel to serve the half past eight Mass, I found him in a trance. He'd be kneeling on a step in front of the altar staring at the tabernacle deep in prayer. There would be a look on his face that was not of this world – as if an inner radiance had perfused his being. When I saw him like that, I knew there was something special or holy about the man. I'd go into the sacristy and bang things about for a minute or two until he came to his senses. Nobody would have dreamt of approaching or touching him to bring him round. He needed to return to the real world in his own time.

Canon Creen had a quick eye for a sinner. It was no good telling him a lie or trying to cover up something you'd done. He'd fix you with his hypnotic eyes and say, "Now, James, I want you to tell me the truth. Did you spill the altar wine?"

All the altar boys felt compelled to tell him the truth even if it meant getting into trouble – but once you told the truth he almost always let the matter drop.

Confessions were on Saturday and there were always a lot of people. I was the last penitent one evening and was coming out of the Chapel with the Canon when an old man came struggling up the hill on his bicycle.

"What is it, John Joe?" the Canon asked.

"I was hoping to get to confession Canon but I got a puncture and was delayed."

"Go on home, John Joe. You're an open book. There're no sins on your soul. Come back next week and I'll hear your confession then. It's boys like those lads over there," and he nodded towards a couple of corner boys who were loitering near by, "that should be confessing every week, not you John Joe."

I wondered at the time had John Joe's quick pardoning anything to do with the Canon's rush to hear the days football results on the radio.

When there was a dance in the parish hall, the Canon patrolled it like an anxious father brandishing a blackthorn walking stick. If he saw a girl sitting on a boy's lap, he'd tell her to get off. "Have you no seat of your own?" he'd ask. "If that boyo was a gentleman, young lady and cared anything for you, he'd give you his seat and let you sit on it and guard your holy purity."

When the dancing started he became more vigilant and if he spotted a couple dancing too close, he'd go over and push his stick between them.

"If you're feeling the cold that bad, young man and need to snuggle up to this young girl for a bit of warmth, I suggest you wear a woolly vest next week or stay at home beside your own fire."

Willie John O'Neill was convinced the Canon was a saint. He was his best altar boy and served Mass with great devotion for twelve years. He tried to teach a lot of other altar boys how to serve Mass with the same devotion though not always with the same success.

As far as Willie John was concerned, his conviction that the Canon was special was confirmed the day the Canon cured his uncle of cancer. Willie John had driven the Canon to his uncle's house to administer the last rites. His uncle was in a coma and not expected to last the night. The Canon went into the room and put his hand on the dying man's forehead and began to pray. He gave him a blessing and then turned to his wife and said, "He'll be at Mass next Sunday." He walked to the door. "Where's his pipe, Willie John?"

"It's on the mantelpiece, Canon," he replied.

"Well go and get it and give it to him. He'll want it in five minutes time."

"But Canon, my uncle's dying. He doesn't need his pipe."

"Do what you're told, Willie John," the Canon said sternly.

Willie John went to fetch the pipe although he felt it was a waste of time. When he came back, he was amazed to see his uncle struggling to sit up and calling for his pipe.

The Canon stopped driving on his eightieth birthday and after that he called Willie John whenever he wanted to go anywhere. Willie John was so convinced Canon Creen was a saint he dropped whatever he was doing to take him wherever he wanted to go. Mostly the calls were to the sick and dying. The Canon would bring them Holy Communion. He had a deep belief in the Real Presence, that Christ himself was present in the host of Holy Communion which a priest consecrated during Mass. He refused to speak to anyone when he was carrying Holy Communion in deference to the Real Presence.

One Sunday, Willie John was playing in goal for the parish football team against a rival parish. Willie John's presence was vital to the game. He heard someone calling and turning round, saw the Canon coming up behind the nets.

"Come on Willie John, get your motor. I've to bring the Blessed Sacrament to a dying man."

"But I can't leave, Canon. We've just taken the lead and if I leave we'll lose and they'll blame me."

"What's more important, Willie John, your football game or a man's immortal soul?"

Willie John knew there was no point arguing. He grabbed his clothes and followed the Canon.

"You start the engine up and I'll go into the Chapel and bring out the Blessed Sacrament" the Canon said.

Willie John was waiting at the Chapel door when the Canon came out and they set off, neither of them speaking in the presence of the Blessed Sacrament. They drove for a mile until they came to a T junction.

"Canon....." Willie John said.

"Silence," the Canon shouted, "you are in the presence of the Blessed Sacrament, Willie John. You should know by now not to speak."

"But Canon..."

"Silence I said," the Canon retorted.

Willie John took a deep breath and gathered his thoughts before blurting out, "Canon, I have to talk because I don't know which way to go."

The Canon frowned and silently jabbed his finger left.

When I returned to Clonavon I understood why my father always referred to him as his guide, philosopher and friend. That about summed the man up.

Canon Creen gave me a lot of valuable support during the few remaining years of his life. Despite his irascibility and impatience, I believed he was a saint in the making. I was particularly grateful for his help when I came up against the most vindictive man in the village.

A Contrary Man

Nobody knew anything about Ismael Maddon. No one had any idea where he came from or why he settled in Clonavon. He had a slight brogue that meant he probably originally came from the Republic of Ireland, though this was by no means certain. He pronounced some words in a more English way than Irish.

There's one thing about Irish people and that is they're neighbourly but Ismael wasn't like that. He had no interest in his neighbours or in anyone in Clonavon. He kept himself to himself. He didn't seem to want anyone to know anything about him. There were several people who were only too happy to invent a past for him. It was said a distant relative who lived in Clonavon had died leaving no will many years earlier and that Ismael had got to hear of it and moved into the disused farm.

He had a lot of work to do fixing the derelict farmhouse. He did it all by himself, then tackled the long neglected farm until he had it in working order. After that, he appeared to do very little. He kept a few cows but nobody ever saw him at the local cattle market. He hardly spoke to anyone in the village and any conversation was curt and to the point. He had an Alsatian dog that, even he, found hard to restrain. He called it Gore. Nobody visited him except for a cousin from County Louth. Everyone else was frightened to go near his house because of the angry, out of control, Gore.

Nobody knew where his money came from. It certainly wasn't from farming. There was a rumour he had a lot of money from his time as a mercenary soldier in Africa. Another rumour had him working with a German oil Company in South America. There was a lot of speculation about Ismael Maddon but few facts.

When I was a boy, his arrival in the village caused a minor sensation especially when he rudely refused any offers of help. I was climbing a tree in the front lawn of our house one summer's afternoon when the breadman came whizzing up our avenue in his bread van, a lot faster than usual.

Barney the Breadman (his real name was Hubert Feeny) was not renowned for speed. He ambled along so slowly we used to pass him on our bicycles. This irritated him and that made us enjoy it all the more. That day he jumped out of the van, a considerable achievement for a man of his bulk. He rang our front door bell, keeping his finger on the buzzer.

My mother opened the door and saw that Barney was upset. His big red face was glistening with perspiration. He ran his hands through his ginger hair and hopped from foot to foot in agitation.

"Are you alright, Barney?" my mother.

"I'm right enough Mrs Griffin. Would you like your usual bread?" he blurted out in a shaky voice.

"Are you sure you're alright Barney? You look as if you've just seen a ghost."

"No, I'm alright Mrs Griffin, I'm as right as rain. I'm just a little upset but it'll soon pass."

Even with my inexperience and from my precarious position at the top of a tree, I could see that Barney was far from being alright.

"Come in now Barney and I'll get you a nice cup of tea and we'll soon get you settled down," my mother said soothingly.

"Thanks very much, Mrs Griffin, for your kind offer but honestly I'm alright. I have to keep going and get my rounds finished. I'm late as it is after what's happened." He paused for a second or two as if unsure whether to go on or not.

"Do you by any chance, know a man called Ismael Maddon, Mrs Griffin?" he asked.

I saw my mother hesitate. She knew Ismael only too well. My father once had a run in with him and as a result Ismael didn't speak to him or my mother or any of our family.

"I sort of know him Barney," she said cautiously "though not really that well to be truthful."

"Well, I know him very well. He's one ignorant man if ever I met one and as you know Mrs Griffin, I don't say that too often about anyone. I do my best to be charitable about people but Maddon's pushed that charity beyond my limits. I know it's not right me speaking badly of him but I think he'd test the patience of St Patrick himself.

Since he came to Clonavon I've been driving a mile out of my way every day to deliver him his newspaper. I don't get a penny for my trouble. I do it to be obliging. He rarely buys any bread off me, just takes his paper with a grunt and walks off and never a word of thanks. I can't even get out of the van to give him the paper with that ferocious animal he keeps. It snarls and snaps at me like it wants to take my leg off." Barney shook his head despairingly. He wasn't used to dealing with men like Maddon.

Barney was a generous man. He worked as a breadman but he was much more than that. He took time to listen to lonely old men and women who bought less off him than it cost him in petrol to visit them. He threw in an extra loaf of bread to poor families with a lot of mouths to feed and saved their dignity by saying it was a special offer. He delivered newspapers as a courtesy for McSweeney and a lot more besides to people who lived in outlying farms. At Christmas,

126

you'd see the passenger seat full of plucked turkeys he was delivering for farmers who had enlisted his help.

That day Barney didn't look his usual jolly self at all. He took a deep breath and continued "I went up to Maddon's this morning Mrs Griffin, and to tell you the truth, I thought his mad brute of a dog was going to rip the arm right off me. When I opened the window to hand Maddon his paper, he did nothing to stop the animal from jumping up and snapping at me. I had to keep jerking my arm out of that foaming brute's way while the lazy fool sauntered over for his paper."

"Would you mind getting your dog to settle himself down a little bit, Mr Maddon?" I asked politely.

I couldn't believe the way Maddon reacted. You'd have thought I'd laid ten curses on him and his family the way he went on. He rounded on me like a deranged man, his eyes blazing with fury.

"Don't you tell me what to do with my animal Feeny. He's more right to be in this yard than you. Get yourself out of here right this minute and don't come back. If I ever see you on my property again with your filthy bread cart and your stale bread, I'll set Gore on you."

Barney prided himself on having the freshest bread of any breadman around. He got up at 5.00am to collect it from a baker in Belfast. The affront to his professionalism as well as his kindness was a low blow.

"I'll never set foot on that man's property again, Mrs Griffin, not if you were to offer me a thousand pounds," he said with feeling. "No, not even if you were to offer me a king's ransom. Maddon can get his own paper from now on as far as I'm concerned from wherever he likes but it'll not be from me."

My mother insisted Barney come in for a cup of tea despite his protests. When my father came back from his calls half an hour later, Barney was still distressed. My father gave him a dollop of whiskey and drove him home. Barney left his van outside our surgery overnight. That set a lot of chins wagging. One of the stories doing the rounds was that Barney had taken a heart attack at the doctors and the doctor was seen bringing him to hospital.

By the time I came back to work in Clonavon, I had forgotten about Ismael. I was soon to be reminded of him.

One very wet afternoon on my way home from a call I saw a tall man with a military bearing walking along the road. Despite the teeming rain, he walked ramrod straight. I didn't recognize him and pulled over. "Would you like a lift?" I asked as I opened the door.

The man clambered into the passenger seat without speaking, spraying water everywhere. I thought his behaviour strange as I turned to look at him. He was already staring at me. His black eyes were lifeless like a shark's. He had a lean, tanned face that whould have been handsome if it hadn't been ravaged by bitterness. It was the most unpleasant face I'd ever seen.

"Where are you going?" I asked wishing I'd never stopped.

"I'll tell you when you need to know," he sneered and pointed ahead. It was an order to drive on. He pulled a cigarette from an inside pocket, lit it with a deft movement and blew a long stream of smoke against the windscreen. I was so taken aback, I couldn't speak.

We drove in complete silence for two miles. He flicked the ash from his cigarette onto the car floor. He looked so nasty, I was afraid to confront him.

"Pull over" he suddenly shouted and thumped the dashboard.

I jammed on the brakes and the car skidded to a halt at the entrance to a long tree lined lane. He jumped out and stalked up the lane without saying a word or giving a backward glance.

When I got back to the surgery, I was shaken by the man's rudeness. I told Ida about the incident.

"That can only be one man" she said immediately "Where did you pick him up and where did you leave him off?" When I told her she laughed. "I knew it. Ismael Maddon. James, you've just had the honour of giving a lift to the strangest man ever to set foot in Clonavon. Your father had a bit of a run in with him a few years back and he wasn't exactly bouncing out of his skin after it either. You'll have to get him to tell you about it sometime"

My father phoned a few nights later to tell me he was thinking of extending his holiday for another month or two. I was a bit stunned by the news and asked him why he now needed four or five months holidays when he had originally asked me to do a three month locum.

"Ah well now, your mother's having the time of her life isn't she. She's never had a proper holiday before and she wants to go to Canada to see your sister Johanna. She's always wanted to see a Canadian winter."

"So you're not enjoying yourself then?" I couldn't resist asking. "You're only doing it for my mother?"

"Ah now, don't you know, I like to see her happy James and I know you do too. I can put up with it for her sake" he answered glibly.

"I'm sure you can," I thought to myself.

"Aren't you glad she's so happy? Now will you do it for your mother or not? There could be a bonus in it if you play your cards right and it's great experience for you into the bargain."

"Ok, I'll do it." I replied as I thought my father could teach me a thing or two about manipulating. He sounded relieved until I remembered to ask him about Ismael.

"Do you happen to know a gentleman called Ismael Maddon by any chance?"

There was an angry snort down the phone.

"Maddon? I know him alright. He's one boyo if ever I met one," he said with feeling.

"Why do you say that?"

"I'll tell you why. The Canon and I were standing outside McSweeney's shop one day ten or twelve years ago, having a chat about Lucifer's empty throne in heaven being taken over by Saint Francis of Assisi when out comes Maddon. I'd hardly seen him before in my life and had never spoken to him."

"Well, would you look at the two holy Joes, standing there discussing so-called religion," he says. "I've an intellectual question I'd like to put to you two educated gentlemen, if you don't mind. I'll put it to you first Paddy because you look the dimmer of the two which is saying something. Do you think you could answer it?" he said looking at me. The cheek of him talking to me like that and calling me Paddy.

"It depends what the question is, Mr Maddon" I said as politely as I could.

"It's a medical question, Paddy and maybe even a bit theological, a bit of a brain teaser I'd call it. I'll start you on it anyway. I've a bull in one of my fields that's causing me no end of a dilemma. He's an awful lot of wind coming out of him whatever the cause of it and the noisy flatulence sometimes keeps me awake at night. What do you think I should do with that lump of a bull, Paddy me boy?"

"I'm not qualified to speak about bulls, Mr Maddon." I said. "You should maybe consult your Vet."

"My Vet!" he snorted in disgust, "He knows as much about veterinary work as you know about your doctoring."

He turned to the Canon.

"And you, Danny boy Creen, man of the cloth and very knowledgeable by all accounts by them that knows nothing. What would you do with a bull full of wind?"

I'll tell you something, James I learnt a lot that day about humility, humour and turning the other cheek from the Canon. He kept perfectly calm as though it was a question he was asked every day of the week. He reflected for a few seconds before replying.

"It seems to me there are a couple of options here Mr Maddon," he said. "You could try moving that bull to a more distant field or if he's as full of hot air as you say, you could consider giving him a fig roll or two and see how that worked out. You could maybe consider taking one yourself while you're at it."

A few customers had come out of McSweeney's and had gathered around to hear what was going on. When they heard the Canon's answer they burst out laughing. Ismael went as red as a beetroot. I never saw anybody get so angry over a little teasing and teasing that he had started. Ismael stormed off in a fury and he's never spoken to me or the Canon since. Frank Johnston told me the only time he ever saw Maddon laugh was when his neighbour's barn burnt down after it was struck by lightning."

"Calling the Canon 'Danny boy Creen' must have put the Canon's Christianity to the test," I said. I always like to hear how goodness stands up against trials.

"It did but the Canon came up trumps. He ignored the insults and every time he sees Ismael, he greets him but never gets a reply."

My father continued, "I don't understand why the man behaves like he does and cuts himself off from the community. He goes out of his way to annoy people. It seems to give him some sort of a kick, like when he heard one of his neighbour's set of piglets died and he sent him a Remembrance card. Another thing that shocked me was how he kept crows off his fields by shooting them to wound them and then hung them upside down from trees when they were still alive to scare other crows away. Someone reported him and the police went to investigate but they didn't get too far. Investigating anything on Ismael's land is a dangerous business because of that savage dog of his. He stops anyone going near his property with a sign at the end of his lane. Did you ever see it James?"

"No I didn't" I replied

"Well I'll tell you about it. It has the face of a ferocious Alsatian painted on it, dripping saliva and blood from its mouth. Underneath is written in red "My dog can reach the end of this lane in seven seconds. Can you?"

"What do you think of that for a carry on?"

Before I could say a word he went on. "Take my advice and keep well out of his way."

I decided to take his advice though I did mention Ismael to the Canon when I bumped into him a couple of days later. The Canon was his usual charitable self and refused to say anything bad about the man even though he knew Ismael referred to him as 'Danny boy Creen' or 'that fool, Creen'.

"I'll tell you a couple of amusing things about Ismael" he said with a great laugh. "I was going past his farm on my daily walks a few years ago now, when I spotted him in one of his fields. He was sitting on the grass, with his back against a tree, reading a newspaper. As I passed I nodded at him and was amazed to see he was reading the German newspaper, 'Die Welt.'

I was surprised, not only by him reading a German newspaper but also by the fact I had been trying to get a copy of that paper myself for a long time from various newsagents, even contacting newsagents as far as Dublin.

Before I knew what I was doing I blurted out, "I see you're reading Die Welt, Ismael."

"What's it to you?" he said.

"Well it's just that I'd love to get a copy but I don't know where to buy one. If you don't mind me asking, where did you find your copy?"

"I found it under a tree," he answered sarcastically.

"Found it under a tree? That's an unusual place to find a newspaper, Ismael, never mind a German newspaper. I wonder how it could have got there." I said as pleasantly as I could. I knew the Lord was testing me, James. It was my duty to eat humble pie.

"I'd say a leprechaun put it there," he said with one of his rare grins, "and, by the looks of it, a German Leprechaun. I'll tell you something, James. There's never a dull moment when Ismael's around."

The Canon laughed and launched into another story.

"Another fine summer's evening, I was passing the end of Ismael's lane when a donkey started braying long and hard as they sometimes do, for reasons best known to themselves. Ismael happened to be coming down his lane and, spotted me. He broke his rule of not speaking, "Oh Danny boy" he called out, "by the sound of things there's a clergyman hereabouts in some distress. Can you tell by the roars of him if he's a Protestant or a Catholic?"

I stopped in my tracks and listened attentively as if giving the matter some serious thought.

After a few seconds I turned to Ismael and said, "No. Ismael I think you might be wrong there. That sounds more like a donkey and by the state he's in, I don't know if he believes in any religion at all."

Ismael stamped off in disgust. He doesn't seem to like anyone getting one over on him – a bit like us all I suppose."

I decided to take my father's advice and give Ismael a wide berth. Despite that, Ismael managed to make a fool of me – and that was even after he'd died.

Beyond the Grave

Ismael found out who I was and immediately included me in the list of people he didn't speak to simply because I was my father's son. From then on he ignored me. He never spoke to me or acknowledged me if I passed him on the road. The only person Ismael seemed to get along with was a cousin from Dundalk called by the unlikely name of Jehroe. He'd meet Jehroe in a pub in Banbridge from time to time and the two of them would get completely plastered.

I happened to be in Banbridge one day when they were having one of their soirées. I literally bumped into them as they staggered out of a pub. Jehroe gave me a surly look and squared up for a fight. I kept my head down and moved on rapidly, trying to figure out who looked the least pleasant of the two. I decided Ismael lead by a short head but there wasn't much difference in the two. They looked what they were, thoroughly unpleasant and disagreeable men. Concern about whether Ismael liked me or not was low on my list of priorities but by the turn of events about to unfold, his dislike of me was obviously high on his.

That day in Banbridge was the last time I saw Ismael alive. The next time I saw him he was in a coffin.

I had been working in Clonavon four months when I heard "on the street" that Ismael had been diagnosed with a highly malignant lung cancer. His outlook was poor, measured in weeks rather than months.

He insisted he wasn't going to hospital for any treatment and refused to let the district nurse into his home, even though he was in need of nursing care. His GP, Dr Gibson, went to see him every evening at ten o'clock and gave him a shot of morphine to ease his pain through the night.

Jehroe came up to stay with him. I think he found the going tough. I don't know whether he did it out of duty or love but one thing was sure, he was the only one who had any chance of being left the farm. I reckoned my chances of getting it were even poorer than the Canon's.

No one knew what religion Ismael was. It was rumoured one of his parents was a Protestant and the other a Catholic. Canon Creen made an attempt to see him. He drove up the long lane and met a surly looking Jehroe at the door.

"I've come to see Isamel," he said, "I believe he's not well."

"Ismael doesn't want to see you or the likes of you. He's had enough of hypocrites interfering with his life," the cousin sneered "and I'll tell you another thing Creen, I've just tied Gore up but if you're not off this property by the time I cross the yard, I'll let him off and I'll not be responsible for his actions." The Church of Ireland minister got the same treatment which at least showed Ismael wasn't a bigot.

Everyone was shocked by his rejection of religion, especially as he knew he hadn't long to live.

"Wouldn't you think he'd make his peace with God before he slips his mooring" a Lough Neagh fisherman, said to Bella.

Rumours abounded about where he was going to be buried. There were rumours about rumours. There was even talk of him being buried at sea or being cremated.

An undertaker was summoned to the house from a distant town – Ismael trusted nobody locally. The undertaker was given a lot of instruction and told not to tell anybody what they were under pain of dismissal.

Ismael died all alone one dark stormy night. Jehroe had gone to Dundalk for an important greyhound race, telling Ismael he had to see a sick aunt.

The same aunt had been buried six months earlier which showed how much the two of them kept in touch with their relations.

The village buzzed with excitement as to what was going to happen to Ismael's body. Some people suggested going to the house to pay their respects but Jehroe dashed any hope of that. He declared the house private. Only the undertaker was allowed through the door to make the final arrangements.

From the way the Jehroe behaved, I suspected Ismael had written a clause into his will to say if anyone saw his corpse apart from the doctor and the undertaker, then Jehroe was to be written out of the will.

In Ireland, the dead are normally buried two days after their death and usually in the nearest cemetery of their religious persuasion. It was thought that Ismael, with his obsessive secretiveness, would have opted for burial in some cemetery amongst his ancestors in the Republic of Ireland or for cremation. Cremations were rare in those days as there were no crematoria in Ireland. Anyone requesting cremation had to be taken over to England which was a lengthy and expensive business.

The village was shocked when it learnt Ismael had chosen to be buried on his own farm. He had picked a field as far away from any habitation as possible and marked a spot in the middle of it. He left instructions that the grave was to be fourteen foot deep and there was to be no ceremony, religious

137

or secular. After the burial, any excess soil was to be scattered around the field and grass sown immediately over the area. There was to be no symbol of any description to mark the spot.

We all wondered at his unusual burial place but particularly at the extraordinary depth of the grave – more than twice the usual six feet for those buried in St. Andrews or Chapel Hill. I asked the Canon what he thought about that.

"Well James," he said. "Of course it's a bit unusual but Ismael being the man he was, and isn't it great God didn't make us all the same or we'd be bored to death with each other, has chosen his own way to be buried. It's another sign of the Lord's great diversity when he created us all. Sure, what does it matter anyway where you're buried as long as you die in God's grace and meet him in the Kingdom of Heaven. We should pray for the happy repose of Ismael's immortal soul and not concern ourselves about the depth of his grave."

"Yes Canon, I agree with you entirely but at the same time, do you not think being buried at fourteen feet is a bit extraordinary no matter where you are buried?" Sometimes the Canon's charity irritated me which made me feel bad later.

"Well to tell you the truth, James, I was a bit intrigued by the depth of his grave myself but at the same time, I felt Ismael must have had his reasons. I have given the matter some thought and there's only one reason I can think of to explain his behaviour. Ismael for all his antipathy to the Church, was a very intelligent and well read man. He would have known that fifteen hundred years ago St. Patrick founded a Church in Clonavon and, in those days, when a Church was established in an area, a Community of monks often followed. There is a historical rumour that at one time there was a monastery built near Clonavon but nobody knows for certain where it was. It

138

was said to have been destroyed by the Vikings in the eighth or ninth Century.

"You have heard it said that St. Andrews stands on what was once the site of a Church founded by St Patrick though the details are lost in the mists of time. I think Ismael was concerned he might be buried in consecrated ground if the original monastery had, by chance, been built on his land all those years ago.

When land is consecrated it is consecrated to a depth of thirteen feet and remains consecrated unless a process of deconsecration is undertaken by the appropriate ecclesiastical authorities. You rarely see a deconsecration in this country but you see it increasingly across Europe which is becoming quite secular. "

Once the Canon got started he was a fascinating man to listen to but he tended to get sidetracked and it looked like secular Europe was about to be a major sidetrack.

"I visited Lisieux, a town in northern France last year and home of that great saint, St Thérèse of Lisieux who is known throughout the world as The Little Flower. Did you know that rose petals fell from heaven onto her convent the day she died on 30th September 1897? I was shocked that L'Eglise St Jacques, the main Catholic Church in the town, though, thank goodness, not the Basilica, had been deconsecrated and turned into an Art Gallery - an Art Gallery of all things and with pictures in it that no self respecting person would look at. And then in Italy …."

I was getting edgy with the Canon's explanations. I was already running late for my evening surgery and it looked like I was going to be given a world tour of deconsecrated Churches. I'd have to interrupt before the Canon talked all day and my feet sprouted roots.

"Sorry Canon but did you say the Clonavon monastery was deconsecrated all those years back?"

"No I didn't. It's not known because nobody knows where it was or if it even actually existed," he said before taking up his theme again. "Now in Italy I got the shock of …"

"And that thirteen foot business you mentioned Canon, how did that come about?" I tried again.

"Am I not about to tell you young man?" he retorted. "You know James, sometimes I think you have less patience than your father and he's no Job."

"The thirteen feet came about …" I sighed with relief. He was back on track "… from a dispute several hundred years ago in Westminster Abbey when a wicked Lord who had tried his best to destroy the Church during his lifetime, insisted he wanted to be buried in the Abbey.

"The ecclesiastical scholars of the time put their thinking caps on and got round the problem of burying a sworn enemy of the Church by making his grave fourteen feet deep – in other words burying him in the Abbey but not in consecrated ground. Everyone was happy with the arrangement especially the Church. The Lord's henchmen had indicated they'd burn the Abbey down if their master wasn't buried as he'd requested. In the end they thought their man was getting preferential treatment being buried so deep.

"I think Ismael must have known about all that and wanted to make sure he was well clear of any influence of the Church. Hence the fourteen feet. I only hope it doesn't collapse in on the poor gravediggers with all that damp soil."

The grave was dug over a period of two days with a lot of effort by two silent men Jehroe summoned from the South of Ireland. They drank two crates of bottled Guinness each as they did their job and left without saying a word. Jehroe said he'd

140

fill the grave himself. There was only one possible hitch to Ismael's plan but smart man that he was, he had foreseen it.

It is not legal in Britain or Northern Ireland to bury the body of humans or large animals except in designated areas. If a human corpse is to be buried in a non-designated area, such as a field or at sea, the body must be examined and declared free of contagious diseases by a doctor.

Ismael had done his homework. One thing he didn't want was to have his request turned down and end up being buried in a graveyard for all eternity beside a lot of people he'd hated in life. He left instructions for Dr Gibson to examine his body after death and issue the necessary certificate stating he was free from infection and could safely be buried in his own field.

Unfortunately, the day he died, Dr Gibson had begun a well deserved holiday and was half way across the Atlantic Ocean on his way to visit his brother in New York, all thought of Ismael behind him. His locum was taking the customary Wednesday half day and I was covering for him. There was nothing else Jehroe could do but call me.

When he phoned I was about to begin the evening surgery. He sounded crabbed. I could see he shared Ismael's affection for the Griffin clan even though he'd never met any of us, apart from that brief encounter in Banbridge

I said I would come up after the surgery, if he could find no other doctor in the meantime to issue the necessary certificate. I gave him the telephone numbers of three GPs and asked him to get in touch with me if he had no success with them. I could only imagine Ismael's fury at being given the clearance for burial by a Griffin.

Jehroe phoned on hour later to tell me "none of those no good waster GPs" were interested in his plight. I wasn't surprised. If he'd used the same tone with them as he had with me they wouldn't have come near him with a barge pole.

I agreed to examine Ismael partly out of curiosity and partly because I knew that's what the Canon would have expected of me.

After the surgery I drove up to his house. Jehroe met me in the yard. He looked surly. Gore was off his chain and going beserk with rage despite his advanced age. 'Another fan' I thought as he leapt like something demented at the side window of my car.

The cousin made no move to lock the dog up, I sat looking straight ahead while Gore ran around in a frenzy.

"He'll not touch you," Jehroe said crossly. I'd heard that comment before about dogs and had the scar of six stitches to prove it.

I sat on. After several minutes he reluctantly tied the dog up. It immediately ran to the end of its chain and stood on its hind legs, baying it's fury, an uneasy sound that echoed down the hillside.

I climbed out of the car and walked towards the whitewashed cottage. I noticed everything in the yard was neat and tidy, almost with a military precision. Jehroe didn't speak as he led me into the house. Inside was sparse but neat for a bachelors home. I caught a glimpse in the hallway of beautifully made model aeroplanes and pictures of armies on the move.

I followed him into a darkened room at the rear of the house. There was no furniture except for an old dresser in one corner. In the opposite corner a plain pine coffin with no markings rested on two undertakers trestles. It was closed. As Jehroe unscrewed the lid, I glanced at the only picture in the room. It was a black and white photograph hanging on the wall

142

above the coffin of a beautiful young woman, dressed in black. She was smiling. 'Who could she have been,' I wondered, 'his mother, a wife, a girlfriend perhaps or just a photograph he found in a market.'

"Make the examination snappy" Jehroe said laconically. He had the same sneering quality to his voice as Ismael. What had the two of them talked about during their drinking sessions I wondered. Had they just sat and scoffed at each other.

I looked down at the body in the coffin. Ismael was dressed in his work clothes and wearing his boots. His arms were by his side, not folded over the chest as is traditional in Ireland. He looked like an outlaw from one of those photographs you see in old Cowboy and Western books where the bandit is dumped into a plain coffin after a shoot out or a lynching.

He had lost a lot of weight and his already thin face was emaciated. Even in death it had found no repose. It looked haggard, unsettled and full of unrequited anger.

I asked the cousin a few routine questions regarding infection and made a brief examination of the corpse before filling in the certificate. As I wrote, I thought of the futile way Ismael seemed to have lived his life. He had left little behind him other than bad memories of an angry man who took umbrage at the slightest imagined offence.

I compared his passing to a woman of the same age who had been buried the previous week in Chapel Hill. Despite a life of unremitting sorrow and hardship, she'd kept her good humour to the end and was loved by all who knew her. Why had Ismael chosen one path and she the other. It was one of life's imponderables.

I'd explained to Jehroe when he'd phoned that the examination was a private matter and not NHS work and that there would be a fee for my time and expertise. He had received the news with a snort of indignation and grudgingly agreed to pay.

Normally, where there's a fee to be paid for declaring someone fit for cremation (in other words making sure the deceased hasn't a pacemaker which explodes when heated) I send a bill for my fee to the undertaker several days later. I had a funny feeling if I sent Jehroe a bill, I'd never see a brass farthing. I handed over the certificate and, at the same time, reminded Jehroe of the fee. I was expecting an undignified haggling match and braced myself for it.

To my surprise, he immediately agreed to the amount. He even smiled. He put his hand into an inside pocket of his coat and pulled out a slip of paper. He glanced at it without letting me see what it was and replaced it. He reached in a second time and pulled out a cheque. He filled in the amount and gave it to me. I glanced at it and was surprised to see it was one of Ismael's cheques and that he had signed it himself. He had even filled in the payee part in my name.

How could he possibly have known it would be me examining him? The man was amazing.

"Well" I thought "I'll figure it out later. At least I've got something from that tight wad for my work and for all his nastiness to my family over the years."

There was something very satisfying about putting Ismael's cheque into my pocket.

Ismael was buried the following day in pouring rain. Jehroe was the only mourner. After the undertaker's men lowered the coffin into the grave they were told to leave. He filled it in by himself.

I lodged Ismael's cheque the next day. Two weeks later my bank informed me the cheque had bounced. Ismael had beaten the Griffins one last time – from beyond the grave.

An Encounter

A few days after Ismael's death, I was on my way in to a patient's house when I met the Canon on his way out.

"Did you make it to Ismael's funeral Canon?" I asked.

"No, I couldn't make it for one reason or another," he said with good humour.

"It was an odd funeral," I said "No religious service and being buried in a field. How will God handle that?."

"You shouldn't preoccupy yourself with that, James," the Canon rebuked me. "Leave all that to Himself. He's got on very well sorting that type of thing out without your help in the past and I think He'll manage rightly now."

I knew I'd said the wrong thing as the Canon launched into sermon mode. Once he got going, he was a hard man to stop. I wished I hadn't spoken. "We should judge no man, James, for we never know what secret burden they carry. The great Catholic convert C. K. Chesterton wrote 'The Church is a house with a hundred gates and no two men enter at exactly the same angle.'

"Christ Himself said 'Judge not that ye shall not be judged' and, 'My House has many mansions,' – meaning I suppose if we were to interpret it in the Irish sense - different horses for different courses."

"Yes, Canon, you're right and …" I said trying to interrupt. He ignored me as he ploughed on.

"One of my Professor of Theology's favourite saying was 'When you die, you'll be surprised at some of the people in heaven and shocked at some of the ones in hell.' No James, you should pray for Ismael's immortal soul and leave his judgement to God. Ismael had, as Philip Larkin so beautifully put it, 'a wrong beginning' and will be judged accordingly." He paused to draw breath and I grabbed my chance "How did Celtic get on at the weekend?" I asked.

"Don't talk to me about Celtic," he shouted, the sermon completely forgotten. "If I could go over to Parkhead, I'd give them a bit of my mind, losing to Motherwell. Did you ever hear the likes of it?"

"Oh no," I thought, "I'm going to get the Celtic sermon."

He was always like that when they lost. If they'd won he'd have slapped his thighs and said, "They won. The Bhoys won, God Bless every green hooped one of them," and he'd have gone off singing.

I got the full Celtic sermon that day with trimmings. It was a long time before I made a judgmental statement again or asked the Canon about Celtic.

The more I got to know the people of Clonavon, the more I enjoyed the work. I met school friends who'd married and had children of their own. I was their family doctor and got to know their children too. That made me feel part of the community and gave me a sense of belonging. After several months I recognized a lot of the people from the village and for several miles around it. It took longer to learn the names and the family connections.

Like most people then, I went to Church on Sunday. I always went to St Mary's at Chapel Hill. It's a beautiful 19th Century building of black stone with a tall steeple and two bells. There's a commanding view of the countryside from outside the wrought iron gates. On a good day you can see down to the shores of Lough Neagh and across to the Blue Sperrin mountains.

The bells were rung on Sunday mornings to summon people to Mass. It normally took two people to ring them with a good deal of effort and sweat. For two years before I came back to Clonavon, an immensely strong man called McCoy had taken over the job of ringing both bells. As in any community some people stand out from the crowd. Tom McCoy certainly did.

He was the biggest man in Clonavon although he was originally a native of Mayo. At just under six foot six, with a barrel chest and flaming red hair, he was hard to miss. He had arms like legs and could carry a two hundred pound fridge up two flights of stairs on his own and tear a telephone directory in two, though not at the same time. Tom said he was a descendant of the Vikings. Nobody was going to dispute the historical accuracy of that with him.

He fancied himself a bit and called himself Bull McCoy. Some of the villagers referred to him as Dull McCoy, though not to his face.

Tom was a wealthy man from working hard and running a haulage business. He liked to boast about his success despite the odds stacked against him. "My teacher at primary school told my parents I was the thickest boy he'd ever tried to teach but that when I grew up I'd be able to lift heavy things," he liked to say. "Well, I'd buy and sell that teacher now."

Tom would arrive early on Sunday morning for the bell ringing. He'd take off his jacket and do a few push ups to warm up. Then it was down to some serious work. For the next twenty minutes, an almighty din echoed out of Chapel Hill and down over the countryside as Tom pulled the two heavy ropes, one wrapped around each wrist. He seemed to be doing his best to pull the bells down from the steeple on top of himself as he lunged at the ropes, beads of perspiration streaming over his big, red face.

One Sunday morning when I was coming out of the Chapel with my brother Brian, McCoy was trying his hardest to deafen everybody.

"Wouldn't you just love those bells to come tumbling down and clobber that eejit," Brian said as we passed through the chapel porch.

"That doesn't sound too Christian of you Brian and you coming out of Mass," I was saying to him when I noticed a young woman talking to some of her friends at the Chapel gates. I had never seen her before.

I instantly forgot Brian and McCoy as I looked at her. She was tall and elegant and had dark shoulder length hair. Her serious face was beautiful when she smiled. She stood very straight and gave the impression of being confident and well in control of herself. There was something about her I couldn't define. Then it came to me. She had a touch of class.

I realized I was staring and turned away.

"Who's that girl over there, Brian?" I whispered.

"Where?" he asked. He hadn't even noticed her!

"Now don't turn around like some half-witted donkey and start staring or she'll know we're talking about her," I said. "She's over there beside the gate."

A couple of seconds later Brian discreetly turned his head.

"Do you not know who that is?" he said scathingly.

"I wouldn't have asked if I knew would I?" I replied. "Stop messing and just tell me who she is?"

"That's Helena D'Arcy."

"That's not Helena D'Arcy. I know Helena D'Arcy. She's a chubby little girl who went to school with Maria." Maria was our youngest sister who had just turned seventeen.

"Well, I'm telling you that's Helena D'Arcy whether you believe it or not. It's eight or nine years since you last saw her. People do change you know," he added sarcastically.

I couldn't believe the change in Helena. It was like a duckling turning into a swan.

The last time I met Helena was at Maria's ninth birthday party.

My mother insisted Brian and I help out at the party and keep twenty two little girls amused for an hour playing dodge ball and rounders and running races while she prepared delicate sandwiches and cream buns.

When the food was ready, she called the two of us to help serve it out. I thought that was way out of order. Entertaining little girls was bad enough for a man of the world who was fast approaching his eighteenth birthday but serving them food as well was a step too far. What would my friends say if they ever got to hear that Mr Cool played rounders with nine year old girls and then served then cucumber sandwiches? I'd have been a laughing stock - the uncoolest man on planet earth.

My mother wasn't a bit interested in what my friends thought nor about me being made to look like a monkey. She ordered me to get on with it.

I grabbed a tray of sandwiches and stormed outside pushing past Brian. "Hey man, I feel bad karma, bad, bad karma. Cool it kiddo. Cool it right down man" he muttered in a horrendous American accent. I didn't answer as I stalked over to Maria and Helena who were sitting together arguing about who had won the most races. I shoved the tray of sandwiches between them.

Maria immediately grabbed the two biggest sandwiches with a practiced eye. I'd normally have been proud of her after all the training I'd given her. When Helena saw Maria take two sandwiches she took two as well. I wouldn't normally have

149

been bothered by their behaviour but I was seething. Someone had to bear the brunt of my wrath.

"Put a sandwich back, both of you," I barked. "You're only allowed one at a time. Did no-one teach you any manners?.."

Maria shoved her two sandwiches into her mouth and laughed as she chewed them. I remember Helena blushed to the roots of her dark hair and quietly replaced one of the sandwiches.

I looked at Maria crossly.

"You're a very greedy little girl," I snapped but that only made her laugh all the more.

I could feel my cheeks go red at the memory of it.

"What is Helena doing with herself now?" I asked Brian as casually as I could.

"Oh, she's a student at Edinburgh," Brian said with a laugh. "She got accepted there at seventeen. Very clever you know. Very, very clever. And in case you're thinking of taking a notion for her she wouldn't be interested in the likes of you. You're far too old, far, far, far too old. Almost an old man and a G.P. as well. If she was interested in anybody it would be a high flyer from Oxford or Cambridge who's going to make a name for himself." Brian loved stirring the pot.

"I never said anything about taking a notion for her," I said defensively.

"Aye but I know by the look of you you're already smitten." Brian smirked.

"I wouldn't say that."

"Well, I'm saying it because it's as obvious as a wart on the end of your nose."

"Oh, I don't think so."

"I know so and I still think Helena wouldn't have the remotest interest in you. She'd like a man with a personality."

150

"Do you think so?" I said

"I know so," he answered.

"We'll see about that." I said defiantly. "Anyway, I know she'd be interested in me if she got to know me."

"Well there's not much chance of that happening, Jimmy my boy. Sorry to disappoint you but I know for a fact she's going back to Edinburgh tomorrow."

I tried to look unconcerned.

"And another thing," he continued, "did I mention she's very clever. Very, very, very clever" Brian was really enjoying himself. "The cleverest girl to come out of Clonavon this many a long day. A lot cleverer than you too, probably twice as clever. Four A's in her A-Levels. Why don't you go straight over and tell her what you got in your A-Levels? That's bound to impress her."

"Very funny," I said. "That's a bit below the belt, Brian. At least my A-Levels were better than yours."

I glanced over at Helena again and turned to Brian.

"I'll tell you one thing though."

"And what's that?"

"I'm going to marry Helena D'Arcy someday."

That finished Brian off. He creased himself laughing.

"That's a good one Jimmy. At least you haven't lost your sense of humour. There's more chance of Bull McCoy becoming a ballerina than of you marrying Helena."

A picture of Bull pirouetting awkwardly across a stage flashed through my mind and made me laugh, despite myself. Helena waved a cheerful goodbye to her friends and walked over to a car with three of her tall brothers. They were all dressed in black and made an impressive sight.

I didn't see Helena again for two months and that meeting was even less successful than the cucumber sandwiches but I did see Bull McCoy, the big bell ringer a lot sooner.

A Double Take

Bull McCoy stalked into the surgery. He was cross. I didn't have to look at him twice to know he wasn't a happy man.

"This is the first time I've seen a doctor in twenty years and I don't intend to see one again for another twenty," he started angrily as if blaming me, "and the only reason I'm here is because I need a medical examination for an insurance company so I can get a bank loan."

"That should be straightforward enough," I said, wondering what was upsetting him so much.

"I've no doubt it'll be straightforward for you," he snorted, "examining me for a couple of minutes and charging me ten quid for your trouble. A nice little earner if you can get it is what you're thinking. It's daylight robbery. I'm telling you right here and now I'm not paying you a penny for examining me. Your father's had my cards for over ten years and he's been paid a tidy pile in that time for looking after me and I've never troubled him once. So, as far as I'm concerned, he's been more than well paid for any medical examination I'll ever need"

Bull glowered at me until I had to look away. I'd never seen anyone so angry about a medical examination before. I was beginning to boil inside myself. There was no point explaining that for the last ten years, twenty four hours a day, seven days a week, including Christmas day and all the Bank Holidays, my father had been available to Bull and his family if they needed him. While Bull got his eight hours beauty sleep every night, my father was often driving up and down dark country lanes looking for patient's houses. When Bull took his family on a Sunday outing, my father waited beside the telephone all weekend waiting for it to ring.

'No Bull,' I thought, 'you haven't got that quite right. You've got more than your money's worth out of my father,' but I said nothing. I was tempted to tell him the fee wasn't just for the examination but for the responsibility that went with it. If I passed him fit and he became ill afterwards, the Insurance Company could haul me over the coals for missing something in my examination – but I didn't say that either.

"Well that's alright then, Mr McCoy. If that's the way you feel and I can see you feel strongly about it, we'll forget any talk of a fee and I'll get on with the examination."

I examined him and found he was as strong a man as I'd ever met. His blood pressure was excellent and he had an unusually low pulse rate which for a man of his age, was a sign of a high degree of physical fitness. The only abnormality I found was a small hernia (rupture) just above his navel. When I pointed it out to him he dismissed it.

"I've had that since the day I was born," he said. "That's no rupture. That's extra muscle on my stomach."

I tried to explain he should have it seen by a surgeon but he wasn't listening. No amount of explaining was going to change his mind. I let the matter drop. You can't win them all.

I signed the forms and told him I'd put them in the post that evening. McCoy stood up looking as pleased as Punch with himself. He was delighted he'd forced me to do a free medical examination. He was a wealthy man and owned a lot of property and a haulage business. £10 would have been peanuts to him. I've found the best people to pay without a grumble are those that haven't got much. They even offer to pay before you examine them while, on the other hand, I'm still owed £10 for a medical examination by a man who buys a new Masserati every two years.

"That's the last time you'll see me in here," Bull McCoy announced as he opened the door. "I think you doctors are a bunch of chancers anyway." He slammed the door behind him and left without a word of thanks.

'And thank you too, Mr McCoy, Mr Bully Boy, Bull McCoy.' I thought as he left. 'Your parting words and slamming the door are going to cost you dear. Listening to cheek doesn't come cheap in my book.'

I sat down again at my desk and reopened the insurance papers. Up to a month before McCoy's visit, patients were expected to pay in cash or by cheque for any private medical examinations. Most doctors don't like asking patients for money when patients aren't used to paying for medical services and some patients don't like paying for what they consider should be a free service.

The British Medical Association (B.M.A.) arranged for insurance companies to add the doctor's fee on to the insurance premium. That meant the fee was sent to the doctor by the insurance company without the doctor or the patient having to mention money.

Bull McCoy was obviously unaware of this new arrangement. I looked at the insurance note which said, 'any reasonable fee will be paid by the company on the completion of this form.' There were not standardised fees then like there are today. The usual fee for an insurance form was £10 or £20 depending on how detailed the form was and how long the examination took. Before the BMA changed this most doctors charged between £1 and £10 according to whether they thought the patient was well off or not. I sent a bill for £20 to Bull's insurance company - £10 for the examination, £5 to help me recover from his cheek and £5 for slamming the door.

My only regret was I couldn't tell anyone about it except my father when he came home. I knew he'd appreciate me getting one over on bully McCoy.

Any time I met McCoy after that, he'd smirk and wink at me. I always smiled back and thought of his £20 lodged in my bank account. It helped to take away the pain of being bullied. It's called 'positive thinking' nowadays.

Fate does take odd turns though. Bull and I were destined to meet again a lot sooner than either of us expected and in a lot less pleasant circumstances.

The Bull

The woman was shouting at the top of her voice but I couldn't hear a word she said. There was something or somebody in the room with her who was making a lot more noise than she was. It sounded like an elephant who had caught his foot in a snare and was trying to tear himself free.

It was another night when I was on call and having difficulty sleeping. I was worried there would be a call out and I wouldn't hear the phone. I must have been dozing for about five minutes when the phone rang. It was half past four in the morning and rain was pelting through the darkness against my bedroom window.

"You'll have to speak louder," I yelled down the phone, "or go to another room. I can't make out anything you're saying."

She finally got the message and went to another room. I could still hear the dreadful bellowing in the background.

"It's Mrs McCoy, doctor, Tom McCoy's wife." She sounded distraught and was speaking so quickly I could hardly make out what she was saying. "You've got to come now. There's something terribly wrong with Tom. I don't know what's happened to him. He can't speak. I think he's dying," and she put the phone down.

'She's not the only one who doesn't know what's wrong with him,' I thought as I threw on my jacket and ran outside to my car. Patients almost always give doctors some idea on the phone of what's the matter with them – so that by the time the doctor goes out to see them, he has a fair idea of the diagnosis and how urgent the call is. All I knew was that Bull McCoy was making an unbelievable amount of noise. I wondered what sort of pain could make a man like McCoy roar like that. I knew he could be a bully but I also knew he had a remarkable tolerance for pain. Someone once told me they'd seen him accidentally drive a nail right through the palm of his hand. He pulled the nail out with a pair of pliers, wrapped a bandage round his hand and went straight back to his job. It must be one awful pain to make McCoy shriek so loudly.

As I raced to his house, I racked my brains wondering what could be the matter with him. It wasn't likely to be a heart attack or a dissecting aortic aneurysm. He was too young and fit for either of those. Both conditions were usually very painful but the patient usually felt too weak to speak, never mind shout. Could it be a kidney stone? That is one of the worst pains known to man. I have seen the hardest of men crying with the pain of kidney stones but McCoy's pain seemed even worse. With kidney stones, the pain comes in spasms about every five minutes. In between the spasms it eases up a little. McCoy's pain sounded continuous. A burst appendix or peritonitis perhaps? Again with either of these conditions he would have been too ill to shout. Gall stones were unlikely in a man as fit as he was and, in any case, pain from gall stones wasn't usually as bad as that. Could it be a twisted bowel? I just didn't know.

As I braked outside McCoy's huge mansion, I heard him roaring before I turned the engine off. Mrs McCoy was waiting for me under the porch. I grabbed my bag and ran. There was no need for her to direct me to the bedroom, I followed the noise as she came after me, telling me what happened as she ran to keep up.

"Tom woke half an hour ago screaming like somebody demented," she said. "His face was as red as a beetroot and the sweat was running off him like a river. He's been roaring like

158

that since and can't even talk, the pain is so bad. If you can't get it to stop soon I think he'll die. Nobody's heart can stand that much pain for long, no matter how strong they are." That news did nothing to settle me or increase my confidence in handling this case. I ran into the bedroom.

Bull was leaning against the back of a chair. He had ripped his pyjama top off and flung it on to the floor. His massive chest was heaving as he gasped for air. He was quivering like a jelly as sweat poured down his back. His eyes were shut and his teeth gritted as he tried to quell a scream. He was one painful looking man.

I went over and stood in front of him. He looked at me with a terrified stare. He tried to speak but before he could say a word, he was hit by a spasm of pain that made him roar in anguish.

"Where's the pain, Tom," I shouted into his ear trying to get his attention. He bellowed and shouted but couldn't speak. In my short medical career, I had never seen anyone in so much pain,

"Show me where the pain is, Tom," I shouted at the top of my voice. "Point to it. Point to where the pain is. Put your finger on where you feel the pain."

He managed to lift his hand to the small rupture I had found when I examined him a few days earlier.

I reached out and touched it gently. He shrieked in pain and rage and rounded on me with his huge fist raised. I thought he was going to plant it in my face.

"I'm sorry, Tom. I didn't mean to hurt you but I can't find out what's wrong with you unless I examine you. I'm going to have to look at that hernia again. It'll take less than three seconds to find out if you can just bear with me."

159

I barely touched his hernia as I examined him again. He grimaced and let out a loud moan. The hernia felt as hard as a rock. It was an angry reddish purple colour.

Bull had a strangulated umbilical hernia. The rupture had twisted on itself when he was sleeping and become trapped. It was no wonder he was in so much pain. I'd have to give him some pain relief before he collapsed.

"I'm going to give you an injection, Tom," I shouted as I drew up morphine. I decided to give it to him intravenously so it would have a rapid effect. I never liked giving morphine intravenously since I was a house-man of one week standing and gave it to a young man who was in agony from a slipped disc in his back. He stopped breathing almost immediately after the injection. Intravenous morphine can, on rare occasions block the breathing centre of the brain and lead to sudden death. It was the most anxious ten minutes of my life as I worked to get him going again.

I gave Tom slow intravenous morphine expecting him to get some relief. It had no effect. I might as well have given him water. If anything he was roaring louder than ever.

Normally intravenous morphine reduces pain within a minute. I noticed when I was doing my house-man's that, sometimes, very anxious patients don't get relief from it. A consultants told us to give those patients a dose of diazepam (Valium). He said it relaxed the patient and gave the morphine a chance to work.

Tom was definitely getting worse. He had hoped the injection would ease his pain and, when it didn't, he panicked. I had trouble giving him the diazepam injection. He was so agitated he kept moving constantly. After several minutes I got the needle into a vein and gave him the diazepam intravenously. A minute later he seemed calmer although he still was in a lot of pain. I asked him if he felt any better.

"Yeah," he said, "it's better but it's still pretty bad." He was just about able to speak.

His wife helped me to get him across to his bed and we got him to lie down. He let me examine the hernia again with only the occasional grimace.

"Look. Tom," I said, "I think I can get your pain to go away completely if you can stay calm for a few seconds. It'll save you going to hospital as well."

"Why? What are you going to do?" he gasped.

"I'm going to press your hernia very gently and try and get it to go back in to your abdomen where it should be. Do you think you could stand me pressing now?"

"Yeah, I think so. I'm feeling a bit easier."

I cupped my hands around the bulging hernia. It was the size of a large plum, a very hard, purple plum. Gradually, I began to milk it back into the abdominal cavity. I felt a sudden pop and the hernia disappeared. Tom stopped moaning at once. For ten seconds, nobody spoke. We were afraid to move in case the pain came back.

Then Tom said in an incredulous voice, "Margaret, Margaret, the pain's gone. I can't believe it. It's gone completely. I felt a pop and that was it. The pain just went. It's unbelievable. It's a miracle."

I looked at him. He was grinning like somebody who had just won the lottery. He moved cautiously in case the pain came back and slowly got to his feet. When he could stand without any pain, he was ecstatic.

"The pain's gone. It's completely gone. It's fantastic. It's incredible. You did a great job, doc." Bull was euphorically happy. He slapped me on the back so enthusiastically I nearly went through the window. A few seconds later, his face clouded over again. The hernia had reappeared, that sinister little bulge around his navel.

"It's back. It's come back," he said, almost hysterical with fear.

"Calm yourself down, Tom," I said. "The rupture I told you about three weeks ago is back but it's back the way it's always been from the day you were born. It's not twisted on itself like it was two minutes ago. You've nothing to worry about."

I explained to him that a hernia was only a problem if it got trapped.

We went downstairs and, despite my advice, Tom poured himself an enormous whisky and drank it back with a gulp. "That was thirsty work that rupture," he said as he emptied the remains of the bottle into his glass. "The thirstiest work I ever did." When I refused a drink, explaining I was on duty, he took a bottle of twenty-year-old malt whisky out of his drinks cabinet and insisted I take it home with me.

Tom was one happy man. He couldn't believe his good fortune. He had gone from thinking he was about to die in agony to feeling on top of the world and all in a matter of minutes.

As he walked me to my car, he came as near to an apology as he probably ever did in his life.

"Do you know something, Doc," he said, "we all say stupid things in our lives and sometimes I think I say stupid things too."

"Oh, I wouldn't think so Tom. I couldn't imagine you doing that."

He laughed and shook my hand.

I drove down Bull McCoy's long drive with its tall lamps shining brightly. I felt almost as happy as Bull did. It was one occasion when my being there made a difference. I hadn't saved Bull's life (though had he been born a hundred years earlier he would have died a horrible death) but I had dramatically altered the quality of it.

As I drove home slowly, the watery winter sun came up behind the Hill of Crewe and cast its rays down over the fields that lay like a tapestry in front of me. I saw black and white Friesian cows gathering around gates waiting to be milked and heard the buckets clanking as the farmers prepared for them in their byres. The dark blue hills of the Sperrin Mountains came into view as sunlight danced on the waters of Lough Neagh.

I suddenly felt that this was the place that was meant for me. tThis was where I belonged.

I only saw Tom once after that for medical reasons. He came to the surgery a week later for a referral letter to a surgeon. He seemed uneasy. As he was going out, he stopped and said "By the way doc, I think I might own you a pound or two for that insurance form."

"No, no, not at all Tom. You don't owe me a penny. Don't worry yourself about that at all," I said as I ushered him out. "I'll tell you what you can do for me though, if you don't mind, you can ring the bells at Chapel Hill the day I get married if we're both still around then." He laughed and shook my hand.

I wondered if it would be Helena by my side on that day. I didn't know what made me mention it to Bull or what brought Helena to my mind. But that's just the way it was!

The Heart Kart

Bull could be many things but one thing you could never accuse him of was being apathetic. Like everybody else, I find it difficult dealing with apathetic people, patients or otherwise. Sometimes they are like that because they are depressed or have developed a mental illness like schizophrenia or because they're suffering from a physical illness such as a poorly functioning thyroid gland or anaemia and have no energy. I have no problem dealing with those people. It's not their fault. But sometimes I find myself face to face with people who make no effort to do anything. They are just plain apathetic.

Canon Creen shared my feelings on the subject. He blasted out a sermon one Sunday about God spitting out the lukewarm. It made a few of the apathetic people in the congregation sit up.

At the same time, he was strong on telling us not to judge anyone other than ourselves.

"If God needed you to help judge the behaviour of others He'd have had you sitting at the right hand side of His throne helping Him out," he liked to remind us. It was one of his better sermons. Unfortunately there were some in the congregation who didn't get the message.

Working with people who are sick or who think they're are sick, teaches you a lot of things. One thing you have to learn and the sooner the better, is not to judge any situation until you have all the facts. Even then, you can get it wrong. I'm still learning that lesson.

One Sunday night, the phone rang when I had just fallen asleep. I had tossed and turned until four in the morning waiting for that very moment. It must have been ringing for a long time because I had incorporated it into my dream and wished someone would answer it. When I realized it was my own phone ringing, I came to with a start and groped for it in the dark. My brain felt as if I was emerging from a dense fog.

"Hello," I said in a voice thick with sleep. I just couldn't summon a cheerful answer.

"Is that Dr. Gibson?" a woman asked.

"No," I managed to answer as I stifled a yawn. "I'm Dr Griffin. I'm on call this weekend. What's the problem?"

"Oh, Dr Griffin, I'm so sorry to trouble you. I was hoping to speak to Dr Gibson. It's my mother again and he knows all about her," she sighed

"I'm sorry, he's not on call tonight."

She had no idea how sorry I was. I was feeling totally shattered after a sleepless weekend on call. The thought of another call followed by a busy Monday morning surgery in four and a half hours time was too dreadful to contemplate.

"Could you help me? I'm concerned about my mother," the woman continued in a voice so low it was hard to make out.

"What's happened to her?" I asked.

"She was up early this morning," the soft voice continued. "and I made her a cup of tea. She took a sip and then grabbed her chest and fell to the floor. I tried to bring her round with cold compresses but they don't seem to be doing any good. She started to make grunting noises a short while ago and her face has gone a sort of blue colour."

The woman's voice sounded remarkably calm for somebody whose mother had collapsed and who seemed, by her description, to be dying.

"When did she start to make those grunting noises?" I asked expecting her to say thirty seconds earlier.

"About half an hour ago, doctor," she said in the same unperturbed voice.

"Half an hour ago?" I said in alarm. "Are you sure she's still alive?"

"Yes, I think so, doctor. I can still hear her breathing but her face is very blue." The woman's voice was as calm as if she was reading out a train time table.

"Do you think I should keep on with the cold compresses for a bit longer and see if she comes round?" she asked.

"I think I'd better come and see your mother straight away. It sounds like she's had a heart attack. Call 999 and ask them to send the cardiac ambulance immediately. I'll be with you shortly."

"Alright, doctor and thank you," she said. There wasn't a hint of panic in her voice. Her mother was dying yet the woman sounded completely unconcerned.

I raced out to my car. It was pitch black and the roads were silent as I drove quickly through the sleeping village and into the countryside. I've had call outs at all times of the night including a few nights when I've worked around the clock. I've always found being woken between three and five o'clock is the worst of all. You feel as if your head has been smacked with a mallet. It takes longer to come round then and for your brain to function. I've spoken to other doctors and they have the same problem.

It's because our Circadian rhythms (the body clock) are at their lowest at that time. That's why so many deaths from asthma or heart attacks occur in the early hours of the morning. The patient's rhythm is at it slowest ebb and has much less resistance to illness.

I wasn't thinking of my Circadian rhythm that morning as I drove up the long lane to the McCombry farm. I was wondering whether Mrs McCombry would be alive or dead when I got there. The anxiety gave me a rush of adrenalin which cleared my head.

As I drove into the yard, I saw two of Mrs McCombry's sons leaning against the wall at the back of the house chatting to each other. They didn't seem in the slightest bit bothered that their mother was at death's door. I think they'd have looked more worried if they'd heard the milkman was going to be late.

They casually pointed to the sitting room when I asked where their mother was.

Usually when I'm called to an emergency like that, one of the sons would have been sitting anxiously in his car at the end of the lane with his lights on to make sure I didn't miss the turning and the other would have raced indoors to direct me to where his mother was the moment I arrived but not those two likely lads. They were the most apathetic pair I ever came across.

I ran into the sitting room and almost stumbled over a small, fat woman, in a dirty pink dressing gown, lying beside the door. She was unconscious. Her face was blue and her breathing loud and snorting. My first thought was that she had less than a minute to live.

Her daughter was kneeling beside her, wiping the sweat off her forehead with a cloth. She was a neat, pleasant looking woman in her early forties, the sort of woman you'd have expected to be extremely anxious about her mother.

"Hello, Dr Griffin," she said raising her head slowly. "Thank you for coming." She leant back on her heels and her eyes drifted off around the room.

Her voice was so calm I half expected her to ask me if I'd like a cup of tea before I started bringing her mother round.

I knelt down beside Mrs McCombry and felt for her carotid artery. It wasn't there. She suddenly gave a huge gasp and stopped breathing. As an intern, I'd worked with the brilliant though eccentric Dr Brennan who had trained us over and over again what to do when someone's heart stopped. He talked about the heart as if it was a faulty piece of machinery like a broken car engine that you had to fix. For reasons of his own he considered all hearts to be female – the way ship's captains and car enthusiast regard their ships and cars as feminine.

"Right ladies and gents," he'd say, "the first thing you do when somebody has just died from a heart attack is give the centre of the chest a mighty thump to see if you can get her going again. You'll be lucky if she does but it's worth a try. If you restart one heart with a thump like that in a lifetime, you'll have achieved something. Mind the elderly and don't thump too hard or you'll break the rib cage. If the thump doesn't work it's straight down to business – lads and lassies - C.P.R. (Cardiopulmonary Resuscitation) cardiac massage and mouth to mouth. If you have any common sense, you'll let someone else get on with the mouth to mouth end of things while you do the massage. Take out the dentures and make sure the tongue hasn't fallen back and is choking the patient. Loosen the collar while you're at it. Start pushing the chest down, not too hard and not too easy. Remember you're trying to make her pump again. You're not trying to crush her or burst her. She's a delicate enough piece of machinery.

"The lad who's picked the short straw and is doing the mouth to mouth needs to give the lungs a blast of air every four or five pumps of the heart. If you have someone who can intubate, all the better. You'd need to do a bit of an E.C.G. pretty quickly to see if she's fibrillating. If she is, there's nothing for it but the jump leads. Get her linked up to the defibrillator and step well back. You don't want a shock yourself. You'll get enough of them in your lifetime. Give her a few joules. That should bring her back into sinus rhythm. If it doesn't, up the joules and give her another charge. In between keep the C.P.R. going. If you're still in trouble, then things aren't looking good. It's time to start the needlework.

"Get the long cardiac needle with the adrenalin into the heart and, if that doesn't work, it's time for the clergy. Death is on the horizon" and Dr Brennan would put the palm of his hand over his eyes as if gazing into the distance, "'And come he slow or come he fast, It is but Death who comes at last' Sir Walter Scott lads. A great man for the poetry."

Dr Brennan had repeated his resuscitation mantra so often I knew it by heart. I went into action straight away. I gave the centre of her chest a thump. To my amazement, Mrs McCombry's heart restarted and she began to breathe again. I could feel her heart thumping wildly against her ribs. It was the only time in all my life I ever restarted a heart with a thump. Now that the heart was going, I began to worry it would beat too fast and slip into ventricular fibrillation. Dr Brennan had a way of dealing with that too.

"Ventricular fibrillation," he'd say in his deep brogue, "needs instant electrics (the defribillator). The heart muscle instead of contracting in a single unit is contracting like a bag of worms – a lot of movement but not enough strength to pump the blood round the body. If you don't get the fibrillation sorted out within two minutes. You might as well call the undertaker. If the electrics fail you, you're looking at death straight in the face or at any rate the patient is 'O Grave! Where is thy Victory? O Death! Where is thy sting' Alexander Pope lads. A wit with dunces and a dunce with wits"

Dr Brennan's daft though reassuring presence seemed a long way off as I asked the daughter to phone and see how long it was going to take the ambulance to arrive.

"Ten minutes they say," she answered as she sauntered back into the room five minutes later.

I asked one of the brothers to go and meet the ambulance on the main road to make sure the driver didn't miss the turning. He ambled off as if he was on a Sunday afternoon stroll. The other brother strolled into the kitchen to make himself a cup of tea.

What was the matter with these people? Urgency didn't seem to be a word in their vocabulary. I couldn't figure it out. I shrugged my shoulders and concentrated on my own dilemma.

Would Mrs McCombry's heart keep going in sinus rhythm or would it break into Venticular fibrillation before the ambulance arrived. In those days, GPs didn't have portable defibrillators. The ones that were available were too big and too costly.

I knew I had to keep the woman stable for at least ten minutes. I inserted a cannula into one of her veins and waited for the ambulance.

Those ten minutes passed very slowly and I wondered if they would ever end. Mrs McCombry was a dreadful colour. She was breathing deeply and rapidly. I tried to measure her blood pressure but it was unrecordable. She was in cardiogenic shock. That meant her heart was beating with just enough force to keep her alive but not enough to distribute blood to her vital organs. Her chances of survival were less than ten per cent. I told the daughter her mother was critically ill and would be lucky to survive.

"It looks like it, doesn't it," the daughter said without any emotion.

170

I breathed a sigh of relief when at long last, I heard the 'Nee, naw, Nee naw,' of the ambulance. As it pulled into the yard. Mrs McCombry suddenly began to breathe in great big sighs. Her face went dark blue, I knew she was fibrillating. I told her daughter to run and tell the cardiac team to hurry. She got up and ambled towards the door. I felt like shouting at her to speed up. After all, it was her mother who was dying.

A white coated doctor and a staff nurse crashed through the door just as she reached it. They were followed by two blue uniformed Ambulance men carrying a load of cardiac resuscitation equipment. They went straight to the patient and slapped leads on her arms, legs and chest. An image of her heart tracing came up and showed venticular fibrillation.

"V.F.," the doctor shouted. "Defib ready. Stand clear."

He placed the two paddles of the defibrillator on Mrs McCombry's chest and pressed a button. A strong electric current passed through her and lifted her off the ground. I looked at the new tracing. There was no change. They prepared for a second shock.

"Charge ready. Stand back," one of the ambulance men called out.

There was a second loud thump and Mrs McCombry was lifted off the ground again. That shock brought her heart back into normal rhythm. She began to breathe in short gasps.

The team worked on her for over an hour trying to stabilize her by getting her heart to slow down and her blood pressure up. They managed to achieve neither which was a very bad prognostic sign. They decided to get her to the Royal Victoria Cardiac unit as quickly as possible if she was to have any chance of surviving.

None of the family seemed bothered when I told them their mother was critically ill. They just nodded as if I'd said, "By the way, on my way here tonight, I ran over your neighbour's tortoise."

The paramedics lifted Mrs McCombry into the ambulance and sped off with the sirens blaring. I left shortly after, thinking what a strange apathetic bunch they were.

A watery sun was struggling to rise above the horizon as I drove home. I had been at the McCombry home for over three hours and was looking forward to a hot shower and treating myself to a bacon and egg breakfast before facing the Monday morning charge. I couldn't remember ever feeling so totally drained and exhausted.

I came round a corner just outside the village and had to brake sharply. A young man was trying to flag me down before I ran over an elderly man who was lying on the road. He had been knocked down a few minutes earlier. A young woman with her back to me was tending to him. Another older woman was coming out of a nearby cottage carrying a pillow and several blankets.

"Oh, no," I thought. "There goes my shower and my bacon and eggs."

I put my hazard lights on and told the young man to go further back around the corner and stop any cars there before they knocked him down too. He wandered off as unconcerned as a donkey in a daisy field. "Really," I thought to myself in exasperation, "some people have less common sense than your average dinosaur." I walked over to the elderly man. As I approached I saw he wasn't badly injured. He was conscious and talking to the young woman who was trying to help him.

I was exhausted, hungry and fed up. The older woman had put a pillow under the man's head and was starting to tuck the blankets around him.

'What sort of set up is this?' I thought. 'Treating a man in the middle of the road is bad enough at the best of times but when he's thirty yards from a dangerous bend and in bad light, it's downright madness.'

"Why don't you pull him into the middle of the road and make sure the next juggernaut finishes him off," I blurted out before I knew what I was saying. The early morning is always a bad time for me.

The older woman gave me an angry look and the young woman turned round. It was Helena D'Arcy.

Helena blushed. "We were afraid to move him, doctor in case he had a spinal injury and we made him worse," she said quietly as she stood up and moved to one side to make room for me.

I could have bitten my tongue off. 'Why, why, why am I such a blathering fool?' I thought.

"I've called an ambulance," Helena added.

I knelt down to examine the old man. He had no serious injuries just abrasions on his arms and legs. He'd been lucky to escape so lightly. I sighed with relief and said a few words to him, then turned to speak to Helena but she was gone. She could only have gone in one direction and my first thought was to follow her and try to explain but that would only have made matters worse. The ambulance arrived twenty minutes later and I was back in time to have a boiled egg before surgery.

I phoned Dr Gibson later that morning and told him about Mrs McCombry's critical condition. I explained what had happened and how we had brought her round, I mentioned the disinterest of her children.

"Ah, yes, James, they've had a lot of trouble with their mother over the last few years. Her husband and one of her daughters were killed in a car crash about ten years ago. She

173

became very depressed and took to the drink after being a teetotaler all her life. She was always afraid of alcohol because her father and three of her brothers were alcoholics. When she started drinking, Mrs McCombry took to it like a fish to water and has been nothing but a worry to her children since.

She must have inherited the alcoholic gene. For the last few years, she's been in and out of an alcoholic haze. Her children never know what she's going to do next. She's often violent when she's drunk and causes all sorts of trouble. There was one night last summer when they couldn't find her after looking for her all night. She was lying in a ditch in a pool of her own vomit. It was lucky for her it was a dry summer or she'd have drowned. She's tried to kill herself several times in the last year and nearly succeeded a couple of times with a mixture of alcohol and tablets.

"Her children aren't a heartless bunch. They're just worn out. Many's a family would have left her to her own devices long ago. They've been more than good to her despite all the trouble and embarrassment she's caused them. That daughter of hers was probably trying to sober her mother up with a cup of tea when she collapsed this morning. I'll tell you another thing James," Dr Gibson said with a laugh, "I don't know if Mrs McCombry is going to be too pleased when she hears she died twice and you and the cardiac team brought her round."

I phoned the hospital that night. Mrs McCombry had taken another heart attack and died shortly after being admitted. I didn't know what way I should feel. Maybe the Canon would have the answer.

The Cat and the Lantern

I had been working in Clonavon for five months when my father phoned from Canada to ask how I was getting on. He wanted to know if I was enjoying the work. I told him it was better than I thought it would be.

"Good," he said, "I'm glad to heat it. Clonavon's not a bad wee spot is it? And do you know something, your mother's in great form over here. She's never had a holiday like this in her life before. It's just what she needed after rearing all you children."

"I'm glad to hear it," I said. I knew he was beating about the bush and wondered what he was after.

"I've never seen her looking so happy and relaxed. And do you know what she just happened to say to me this morning James, she said she would love to stay here in Canada with your sister Johanna a wee bit longer."

"Did she now?" I said cautiously.

"She did indeed. Would you be agreeable to that?" We were getting to the point.

"How long were you thinking of staying, though it's a pity you're not enjoying yourself too," I couldn't resist adding.

"Ah well, I'm making the most of it. I'm doing my best in the circumstances. Would three months be alright?" he said.

"Three months!" I exclaimed. I was expecting him to say a week or two, a month at the most.

"Yes, three months. Your mother thought it would be nice to round the trip up while we're at it."

My father had a habit of not explaining himself fully or of saying my mother wanted something when he wanted it himself. I suppose he thought it didn't make him sound selfish.

"Three months is a long time," I said doubtfully.

"I thought you said you were enjoying yourself."

"I am but not that much that I want to spend eight months here on my own. I'd like a day or two off myself some time you know."

"Ah, don't worry about that. You'll get plenty of time off when I get back" he replied. "Will you do it for your mother, or not? Didn't you just say you liked the work? That's the main thing isn't it?"

"Well, I do but I still don't understand why you want three more months off?"

"Your mother would love to go across Canada by train to see the Rockies. She's always wanted to see them in the spring."

He was up to his old tricks again, putting the blame on to my mother but I was on to him.

"Would she now?" I said. "You're not interested in seeing the Rockies yourself and you're only going by train for my mother's sake." My mother had as much interest in trains as Barney the Breadman's ferret while my father could name every train in Ireland

"Sure, you know she wouldn't want to go without me." He was a hard man to pin down. "Will you do it or won't you? There could be another little bonus in it for you if you play your cards right."

I thought quickly. I was enjoying myself and I was getting to know the people. It wasn't as if I was a stranger. I'd been to the village school for seven years before going to school in Belfast. I'd only made brief visits home when I studied and worked in Dublin and had lost touch with a lot of my old friends. I had the chance now to renew old friendships which was very pleasant. On top of that I was the boss. It wasn't so bad.

"Alright," I said. I could hear the sigh of relief four thousand miles away.

"Good lad yourself," he said and put the phone down. I could imagine him running off to tell my mother as pleased as punch with himself.

When you move out of a community, it's surprising how quickly you lose touch. I didn't know who was married to who and which people were related. That sort of knowledge comes from listening and meeting other people at sporting or Church and social events. I had missed out on all that by being away from home for so long. I had a lot of catching up to do but I had help from Ida and Bella.

Ida knew everybody. She seemed to be related to half of them as well.

If I needed some background information on a patient or if I'd forgotten the name of someone I met in the village, I'd only to mention it when the three of us were having a coffee break.

"I saw a tall, thin man when I was in Nora O'Brien's the other day," I said one morning. "He looked familiar but for the life of me, I couldn't remember....."

"That would have been Tom Reid," Ida butted in before Bella could open her mouth. "he goes pigeon shooting with Mrs O'Brien's son. Tony. He's from Anahilt and works in Insurance. He's married with four children and they're all at school now."

Another morning, I asked who was the woman with the big, pink hat who had gone to John Finnegan's wedding with Andy O'Rourke.

177

Bella was delighted to be the first off the block that day.

"Oh, that's a woman called Hogan. She's not from this part of the world. She's a Dubliner and has a boutique off O'Connell Street. They say she has a pile of money and a great notion for young O'Rourke."

With help like that, I soon got to know a lot of the patients very well and a lot quicker than I would have thought possible. Some of the information was trivial but it was never gossipy and it was often helpful in the most unexpected way.

Mrs O'Brien, the future mother-in-law of the pink hat, rarely attended the surgery. Then she started calling in once or twice a week and, nearly always, with imaginary complaints. I began to think she was worrying about something and was suffering from anxiety but she denied it. One day, I happened to mention I had seen her son with the pink hatted lady. That opened a release valve.

"That fat trollop! What he sees in her, I don't know. She's old enough to be his Granny. She's all dolled up in her pink hats and her red lipstick. Why can't he go back with the nice wee girl he had before that old cow came along. He's going to ruin his life with the likes of her and all her fancy notions."

It didn't take long to figure out after that what was causing Mrs O'Brien's anxiety.

I did joint visits with Bella to see housebound patients, particularly patients dying with cancer. It was gratifying to see how they reacted and enjoyed her visits. With her ready smile and no nonsense manner, it would have been a hard person who did not respond. We discussed medical and nursing problems with the families and talked about any social dilemmas or psychological difficulties they were experiencing.

Bella had been particularly helpful with Honoria when Mrs Pringle was hospitalised. I didn't have to ask her to help. She was the kind of person who was always there when she was needed.

I've always found it difficult to sleep when I'm on call. I keep expecting the phone to ring at any minute. When I was a brand new house-man every call was exciting. I would speed through the dark, silent wards of the hospital to put up a drip at three o'clock in the morning and feel as though I was on an errand of mercy and at the cutting edge of medicine but, after a year, those early morning calls began to lose their novelty.

One morning, after another sleepless night, Ida gave me a message to say Gilbert McSweeney had phoned. He wanted me to call and see one of his customers.

Gilbert McSweeney had his shop in the village but he also offered a home shopping service. He'd sometimes put the shutters of his shop up in the afternoon or get someone to take over while he loaded up his big, blue van and drove around the countryside to outlying farms. Gilbert's van was lined with shelves and filled with every type of food and general goods that anyone could need. If he didn't have what a customer wanted, he would go to a lot of trouble to get it. The country folk depended on McSweeney's mobile unit, as he called it. They had little need to go into the village.

He'd noticed one of his customers, Jack McCardle was not well and phoned Ida to tell her of his concern. With prompting from Ida, I set off as soon as surgery was over. I'd never heard of the man but had written down his address and the directions Ida gave me.

I drove several miles into the countryside before turning on to a narrow road that climbed up the western side of the Hill of Crewe. I didn't see a soul although there were several farmhouses dotted on the slopes. They were set well back from the road. There was nobody about to give me directions.

179

Following Ida's instructions I turned left at a twisted beech tree into a muddy lane with grass in the middle of it. I wondered how Gilbert managed to get his mobile unit round such areas. I kept going until I came to the end of the lane. There was nothing there but a couple of derelict buildings and no room to turn round. I did manage it in the end but got the car spattered with mud in the effort.

I drove back to the main road to continue my search but after a further twenty minutes, I gave up and went back to the surgery. I was annoyed at having wasted the best part of an hour. There weren't any mobile phones in those days and public telephones were few and far between.

When I got back, I told Ida I had followed her directions to the letter but all I'd found was a couple of tumbled down stone sheds.

"But that's where he lives, James," she said.

"Where? There weren't any houses near those sheds."

"But he lives in one of those sheds. I forgot to tell you that."

"He couldn't." I insisted. "Nobody could live in a place like that. They didn't even have a proper roof. I thought you said he has two hundred acres of the best land in the county. He'd hardly live like that if he did."

"But he does, James. That's what I'm telling you. His brother Jim died two years ago and he lived exactly the same way. They had no interest in money or anything to do with it. Jack's interest in life is looking after his cows and his sheep. The animals are fed and housed better than he is. Jack took his brother's death very badly though he never complained. The two of them lived and worked together for over sixty years and never a cross word between them. You'd often see them in their ragged clothes walking through the fields together and looking as happy as the day was long. Since Jim died, Jack has been neglecting himself even more and hasn't been looking so well.

I set off again to look for the shacks. As I started up the car, Ida came running out and knocked on the door, "I forgot to tell you. If he doesn't answer when you knock, push the door open and go in. He's a bit deaf and a bit lazy too. He can't always be bothered to get out of bed to answer the door."

I found the sheds again and parked the car. The view must have been one of the best in Ireland. Lough Neagh glistened in the bright sunshine away to my right and, to my left, I could see the dark outline of the Mourne Mountains.

'You'd think, with a view like that, Jack and his brother would have built a house to match it,' I thought as I stepped out right into a mess of mud and cow dung that came up to my ankles.

That put all thought of beautiful views out of my mind. I tiptoed to the door, avoiding the deeper patches of mud and dung where I could. There was no answer to my knock. I pushed the rotten door open and peered into a windowless room. I was shocked by the dirt. It was the grimiest room I had even seen in my life. There was a huge coal fire burning in the grate that spread light and warmth as far as the door. It was the only cheerful thing in the place. There was no electricity or running water.

I saw a movement on what appeared to be a bed and looked closer. A man with several days of stubble on his chin lifted his head from a brown stained pillow. He was wearing a brown woollen hat pulled low over his forehead. His face was a similar colour and coated with dirt. Everything about the place was dark brown or black.

I realized he had got into bed wearing his overcoat and his wellington boots which were covered in fresh green cow dung. Something on the bed moved and two cat's eyes flashed in the darkness. An enormous tabby cat was lying across the man's stomach. It lifted its head and eyed me cautiously.

"Hello there," the man said. His voice was pleasant and unhurried. "Come on ahead in and take a seat."

He pulled himself up laboriously and sat on the edge of the bed. The cat moved lazily off his chest and sat down beside him. He automatically stroked it behind the ears. I looked at the one grime covered chair in the room and decided I would stay standing.

"What can I do for you, young man?" he asked.

I told him who I was and that Gilbert McSweeney was worried about him and had asked me to call.

"Did he now? That's Gilbert for you, always worrying about other people. There isn't a more decent man in Ireland, north or south of the border. He's always doing people good turns. Anyway, about myself. Well now I suppose I'm not so bad. I seem a bit weak lately, that's all. I've just been finding it harder to do my chores about the farm for the last four or five weeks. I suppose it's my age."

I asked him to sit on the chair so I could examine him. His face was bloated and unhealthy. I pulled down his lower eye-lid to examine him for anaemia. It was almost white, whiter than I had ever seen in any living person - a sure sign of severe anaemia. The slightest exertion seemed to make him breathless. He had difficulty taking off his wellingtons when I asked him to remove them. He wasn't wearing socks and it had been a long time since he'd washed his feet. They were caked with inground dirt. Both legs were very swollen as a result of the heart failure which had been brought on by his severe anaemia.

I looked round the room while he put his wellingtons back on. There was no order of any kind. His bed with the brown stained sheets was beside the fire, I took a sharp breath as I thought of the fire hazard. There was a set of drawers with one leg missing, tilted at a funny angle. Two of the drawers had tipped on to the floor. Empty tins of peas and beans with their jagged lids were scattered all over the place. There was an open packet of white pan bread on the greasy table and a half-eaten tin of beans with a spoon in it beside it. Bread and beans seemed to be his staple diet.

"I'm going to have to send you to hospital to get you sorted out, Jack," I told him.

"Well, if that's what's needed, Doctor, that's what I'll have to do. Would you mind calling in to tell Gilbert McSweeney where I've gone. He'll know to drop in and see that Socrates here is alright," and he pointed to his cat.

I promised to do that and went back to the surgery to phone for an ambulance.

Three weeks later Bella came in and asked me to call and see Jack McCardle.

"He's home from hospital, James," she said.

"How is he?" I asked.

"Oh, the very best. I've never seen him better," she replied.

"Why do you want me to go and see him then if there's nothing wrong with him?"

It had been another disturbed night and I was not in my most co-operative mood.

"Oh, I just thought you'd be interested."

"There's no need for me to see Jack if there's nothing wrong with him. I'll go and see him in the next couple of weeks."

"That'll be too late. Even tomorrow could be too late."

183

"Too late for what?"

"Just too late. Call in today even if you can only spare five minutes and you'll see what I mean," and that was all she was going to tell me.

I had a free half hour in the afternoon between home visits and the evening surgery and decided to call and see Jack. Bella had roused my curiosity.

I drove to the farm and was surprised to see the lane had been cleared of mud and dung. I could hardly believe the heavy rain had washed all that mess away. The overgrown hedges that lined the lane had been cut back and the dilapidated sheds renovated. They had been patched up and given a fresh coat of whitewash. A window had been put in and a new roof put in place. Standing in the doorway with it's newly painted red door was an elegant looking man of about seventy. He had long, snowy white hair and a beard and was wearing a three piece worsted suit. He looked like a gentlemen farmer.

"Ah, Dr Griffin," he said. "It's very nice of you to call."

I had never seen the man before in my life. How did he know my name?

"I've come to see Jack McCardle," I said. He put his head back and roared with laughter.

"That's a good one, that is Doctor," he said. "I'm Jack. I'm the man you're looking for."

I looked at him in amazement.

"Some of the nurses said I clean up extra well and I can see you're thinking the same," he said and laughed again.

I went into his home and looked round. It was spick and span. The walls had been scrubbed down and white washed. New furniture had been installed. There was even a vase of flowers on the pine table and a waste paper basket in the corner.

184

I could see the first sign of the old Jack emerging. An empty tin of sardines lay on the floor beside the basket. His throw to dunk the empty tin had missed its mark and there the tin would lie to the end of time or until whoever had cleaned his house swept it up. The new window brought light into the room and the view through it across to the Mourne Mountains was stupendous.

"Who cleaned the house for you, Jack?" I asked, hardly able to believe it had all been done in the three weeks Jack had spent in hospital.

"Gilbert McSweeney did a bit of a tidy up while I was away and his wife gave him a hand. You can always tell a woman's touch. It's a great job altogether they've done. It's an awful pity it won't last but that's the way I am and, unfortunately, that's the way I'll remain. God alone knows why he made Jim and me so untidy in our make up but He did, though to be truthful, we can't blame Him entirely. It must be in the McCardles, that ole laziness."

There are times in life when you come across real goodness so much that you are only too aware of your own shortcomings. It was that feeling that overcame me then. I was touched by Jack's honesty and overcome by the kindness and charity of Gilbert McSweeney and his wife. In my time at Clonavon, I have come across many such instances of neighbourliness and generosity, often to complete strangers, which never fails to impress me. I have come across instances where there has been a distinct lack of neighbourliness too but that's less frequent and another story anyway.

As Jack showed me to the door, he reminded of Anton Mor, a man I treated when I worked in County Kerry. They were both 'natures gentlemen'. I stood with him for a moment on his doorstep and gazed at the magnificent view of Lough

185

Neagh glistening in the sun and the shadows in the Sperrin mountains.

"That's a great view you have, Jack," I said. "I've never seen better,"

"Aye, that's what your father says every time he comes up here."

"Does he?"

"Aye, he does and I always say the same thing back to him."

"And what's that?" I asked expecting him to say something philosophical or poetical at the very least.

"I says, I haven't much time for views myself, doctor and if there's one thing I've learned in a long life that is - You can't eat a view. A view doesn't put food on the table or not for me it doesn't anyway"

"Oh," I said.

"The work has to be done and if you have a notion for it after that, you can talk about views until the cows come home."

Jack might not have been poetical but he was certainly practical.

I called to see Jack every four or five weeks and each time I called, he was a little dirtier and the house a little grimier. No matter how dirty he was, he was always a gentleman and a pleasure to talk to. Like Gilbert McSweeney, he never had a bad word to say about anyone.

One morning Gilbert phoned at eight o'clock. He sounded anxious.

"Can you come and see Jack at once, doctor. He's been badly burnt and in a lot of pain. I've sent for an ambulance.

I ran to my car and hurried to Jack's home. I don't think I ever drove so fast along those narrow lanes and prayed I wouldn't come face to face with a herd of cows or a flock of

186

sheep round one of the sharp corners. As I pulled up in front of the house, Gilbert rushed out to tell me what had happened.

"It was very cold last night and I called round to see if Jack was alright about ten o'clock. I made sure his fire was well stacked up. The weather forecast said there'd be a drop in temperature to minus twelve in the early hours of the morning. I left him with a blazing fire to last the night but, apparently, in the early hours of the morning Socrates jumped off Jack's chest to chase a rat that had come in through a hole in the window. That cat helps to keep him warm and when she didn't come back, Jack lit the Tilley lamp and went out to look for her. By the time he came back, he was frozen to the bone and the fire had gone out so he got back into bed and put the lamp on his chest to give him a bit of warmth. He fell asleep and the lamp fell off and set fire to his clothes and the bed. He managed to put the fire out but he was badly burnt. He lay in agony all night until I called in and found him lying here this morning.

I examined Jack while Gilbert talked. I drew up a syringe of morphine and gave him an injection. He had extensive burns that had made his clothes stick to his flesh. He never complained as the ambulance men lifted him on to a trolley and took him outside. He kept apologising for all the trouble he had caused and thanked Gilbert and myself repeatedly. I didn't think he would survive but, eight weeks later, he was back home again, clean as a new pin but with slightly scorched white hair.

Gilbert had the house cleaned up and repainted. His charity was greater than my optimism. He'd even bought an enormous fire guard. The following summer, I noticed the fireguard blocking up a hole in Jack's hedge. Jack had used it to prevent some bullocks from escaping. He evidently felt their need was greater than his.

On Call

When I was on weekend duty, my freedom was curtailed. I had to stay within earshot of the phone for seventy-two hours. My father had a loud bell installed outside our home so I could at least sit in the garden if the weather was fine. I'd rush indoors to answer the phone when it rang. I can only imagine that some people thought I spent the whole weekend actually sitting beside the phone.

If I didn't answer it immediately, they'd put it down and ring again a few minutes later. I lost count of the number of times I dashed across the lawn and the bell would stop as I put my hand out to pick up the receiver. Thinking it couldn't have been important, I'd return to my deck chair and book, only for it to ring and I'd go through the whole procedure again.

When I went out on a visit I left a recorded message giving an estimate of the time I would be back. Being confined for such long periods made me claustrophobic and fed up.

It was a lot easier when one of my brothers or sisters came home for a break. I'd go for a walk and they came and found me if there was an emergency. One weekend, I was delighted to get the chance to go out for a walk while Maria minded the phone. I had gone about five hundred yards when she came after me in the car. A patient had taken a bad asthma attack. Fortunately her son was able to bring her to the surgery immediately where I treated her. If I'd been twenty minutes later, I think she'd have died.

Most weekend calls were for children with high temperatures or for elderly people with chest or urinary infections. The majority of night calls were for emergencies like Mrs McCombry but occasionally they were for extremely trivial reasons. Some of those calls make me smile when I think of them now but they didn't at the time.

An old lady once phoned at half two in the morning. I recognised her voice immediately, partly by the way she shouted down the phone. She was extremely deaf and intensely anxious. Everything that happened to her was a 'crisis' and every crisis had the potential of putting her into 'a state'. When she got into a state it took a lot of time and tablets to get her back to just a crisis and then back to her normal anxious self.

"Hello, Mrs Gardiner," I said, "what's the crisis?"

"Is that you, Dr Griffin? How did you know it was me and that I was having a crisis?"

I was able to hold the phone a foot away from my ear and hear every word she said. I'd had this conversation with her many times before.

"I think it must be telepathy, Mrs Gardiner," I told her.

"The telly," she said, "you saw it on the telly?"

"No, Mrs Gardiner. What I said was, I was about to tell you," I choose my words carefully before continuing but she didn't give me time.

"Tell me? Tell me what? Have you bad news for me?" She was working herself up into a state and I knew what that meant.

"No, no. There isn't any bad news, no bad news at all" my brain wasn't functioning too clearly at that hour of the morning and I had to think desperately before things got out of hand. "I was about to tell you I've never heard you sounding so…ah…so…ah…so good."

"Good, good. You think I sound good. I don't feel good."

This conversation was getting bizarre.

189

"Well, you sound good to me. Look, Mrs Gardiner, could you please just tell me what the problem is."

"It's not a problem, Dr Griffin. It's a crisis. You told me yourself it's a crisis. Don't you remember?"

"Ah well, it... it must just have slipped my mind for a split second there and of course I remember. Now, could you just tell me what the crisis is?"

"I've wet the bed."

"You've wet the bed," I repeated.

"Yes, I've wet the bed."

"You've wet the bed," I said again "and you phoned to tell me."

"Yes," she said, "I've wet the bed and I don't know what to do."

"You don't know what to do," I repeated at a loss to know how to react to this piece of information.

"No, I don't. That's why I rang you. What should I do?"

She was deadly serious. There was only one thing I could do and that was give her precise advice and hope she understood what I was saying otherwise I was going to end up being on the phone all night.

"Are you still in bed?" I asked.

"Yes Doctor."

"Right. Now the first thing for you to do is to get out of bed."

"Get out of bed at this time of the night and in the middle of winter, are you sure, doctor?"

"Yes, I'm sure. I'm absolutely sure. Now just get out of bed like a good woman."

"Are you sure you're sure, doctor, what with me nearly in a state and all," she asked anxiously

190

"I'm completely and utterly certain," I said firmly, "and you're not in a state Mrs Gardiner, or anywhere near a state."

I was beginning to think it might be quicker if I went over to her house and changed the bed myself.

I heard a lot of shuffling and banging and then her voice shouted down the phone telling me she was out of bed.

"Now I think the second thing you should do is change your night-dress and maybe consider changing your bed sheets."

"What about my vest? Should I change that too, doctor?"

"Yes, that's a very good idea. Change that too"

"I thought that's what I should do but I phoned you just in case and to make sure. Did I do the right thing?"

I hesitated before answering. I knew what I'd liked to have said but thought the better of it. If I said 'No', she'd have spent all night worrying about upsetting me and would have come to the surgery the next morning having another crisis and probably being in a state before the end of the week. I wondered how my father would have answered or Gilbert McSweeney or Barney the breadman. They'd all have said, "Yes Mrs Gardiner, of course you did the right thing".

"You don't think I did the right thing phoning you then, do you doctor?" She wasn't shouting now. A little voice was quivering with apprehension at my failure to reply straight away.

"Yes, yes, Mrs Gardiner. You did the right thing, of course you did the right thing. You can never be too careful in a crisis, can you? I'm glad you called to get it all sorted out."

There was a huge sigh of relief at the other end of the phone.

"Thank you Dr Griffin, thank you ever so much," and she put the phone down.

191

Despite her anxiety, Mrs Gardiner was never rude and was always appreciative of any help or advice I gave her. There were one or two patients who didn't quite reach that standard. Two of them were Ciara Killough and her sister Sharon. Ciara liked to bring her son, Jonathon, to the surgery at least once a week. Nothing was too trivial to escape her attention. If Jonathon had a runny nose or had scratched his ear for ten minutes, it was straight up to the surgery, just in case. Please and thank you were words not included in Ciara's vocabulary. It must have been a genetic defect because her sister, Sharon, who lived next door to her suffered from the same word deficiency. Ciara was ignorant but Sharon was very, very ignorant.

"Is that the doctor's" a cross voice demanded as I dragged myself out of a deep sleep to answer the phone. It was half past five in the morning.

I felt like saying, "No, it's the Donkey Sanctuary in Cork," especially as I had already said it was Dr Griffin speaking when I picked up the phone.

I had already recognised Ciara's voice. It wasn't too difficult. She'd been to the surgery twice that week already and it was only Wednesday.

"Yes, it's Dr Griffin," I said wearily.

"This is Ciara Killough. Jonathon is teething and I've run out of Paracetamol. I want you to bring me over a bottle."

It was an order not a request.

It was on the tip of my tongue to tell her I wasn't a delivery boy but I thought the better of that too.

"When would you like it?" I asked sarcastically. The sarcasm went right over her head.

"Right now. Why do you think I phoned?"

"What happened to the bottle of Paracetamol I gave you yesterday?" I asked.

"I left it at Sharon's."

Sharon lived next door to her. I lived five and a half miles away.

"Why don't you give Sharon a call and get her to drop the bottle round? It shouldn't take her too long."

"I don't want to wake her. She needs her sleep and she gets cross if anybody wakes her. Anyway, it's your job to help people when they're sick. Isn't it?"

I thought I was going to get the standard, 'that's what you're paid for,' line so I interrupted.

"Yes," I said. "It is my job to treat people if they are sick but delivering bottles of Paracetamol at this time in the morning is not usually considered part of my job."

"So you're going to let my wee Jonathon lie here sick all night and maybe die because you're too lazy to get out of your bed to see to a sick, wee boy. You're some doctor ..."

"I have no intention of letting Jonathan die," I said. I could hear Jonathan cooing contentedly as he grabbed at the receiver. He must have been sitting on his mother's knee. He didn't sound too sick to me.

"Are you bringing me the Paracetamol or not?"

"I didn't say I wasn't bringing it, Ciara. It's just that I'd like to ask a few questions about Jonathon first." Ciara would have tested the patience of a saint and I wasn't feeling too saintly just then.

I wanted to make absolutely sure Jonathon wasn't sick before I advised her about Paracetamol deliveries at 5.30am.

"Has Jonathon had a bottle of milk recently, Ciara?" I asked.

"Yeah he has. What do you think eight month old babies eat - steak and chips?" she snapped.

"When did he have his last bottle?" I said trying hard to sound a lot pleasanter than I felt.

"He's just finished one, hasn't he? Are you bringing me that Paracetamol or not?" Ciara seemed to be running out of patience.

"I'm nearly finished asking questions Ciara and I'm doing it for Jonathon's sake after all, so please help me to help the little lad. How many ounces of milk did he take?"

"Eight or nine," she retorted.

"And what's little Jonthon doing now?"

"What difference does that make?"

"I'd just like to know if you don't mind."

"He's playing with a wooden spoon."

Jonathon had just swallowed eight ounces of milk. He was cooing happily and playing with a wooden spoon. In my book, that meant no sick child and no five and a half mile journey at half five in the morning delivering Paracetamol.

"Right then, Ciara, from what you say, Jonathon sounds quite well at the moment."

"Are you bringing the Paracetamol or not?" she shouted. "His little eyes are heavy and if you don't hurry up, he'll be asleep by the time you get here and I don't want nobody waking him up. Do you hear what I'm saying? And another thing, if you see my lights off, it means I'll have gone to bed so don't go waking me up. Just leave the Paracetamol on the door step and don't make any noise." Ciara left me speechless. She was surpassing even her already high standards of rudeness. She was almost on a par with her sister, Sharon.

"Do you understand what I'm telling you," she shouted and slammed down the phone.

I didn't have the same concerns as Ciara about disturbing Sharon's sleep, in fact, quite the opposite. Sharon's sleep needs were at the very bottom of my priority list. One of the advantages about living over the shop so to speak, was that the surgery and patient's notes were to hand. I went down and looked up Sharon's phone number on her records. A very grumpy voice answered my call.

"What?"

"Good morning, Sharon," I said trying to keep the satisfaction out of my voice. "This is Dr Griffin calling. I'm sorry to wake you. It's nothing serious so don't be alarmed."

"What do you want then?" She was waking up fast.

"It's just that people get anxious when a doctor phones early in the morning and I didn't want that to happen to you."

"What are you ringing for then?" She sounded angrier by the second.

"The problem is Sharon, Ciara has run out of Paracetamol for little Jonathon," I said trying to sound concerned but finding it difficult to keep that little note of glee out of my voice.

"What's that to me," she yelled. She was cross now, really cross..

"Sharon, I know how upset you get if anything happens to Jonathan but the fact of the matter is, Ciara wants to give the wee mite some Paracetamol and it seems she left the bottle I gave her in your house."

Sharon's temper was now red hot.

"What's wrong with that brat of hers. She's always going on about how sick he is. There's never a thing wrong with him. He needs a good smack to sort out all that whinging of his."

"I'm sorry, Sharon, unfortunately I can't discuss Jonathon's health issues, patient confidentiality you know." I enjoyed saying that. It made up for a lot of the cheek she'd been giving me and my father since she'd learnt to speak. "As for giving Jonathon a good smack Sharon, you'd really need to discuss that with Ciara and her social worker and Social Services. In the meantime, could you give her a call and drop the Paracetamol round. By the way, she said if her lights are out, it means Jonathon is fast asleep and she doesn't want the little lad woken on any account. She said to just leave the bottle nice and quietly on the door step and don't make any noise. She'll collect it in the morning.

"Is that what she said?" Her voice was surly, very, very surly.

"That's exactly what she said, Sharon. Those were her very words. Goodnight now and thank you for being so obliging."

I put the phone down.

I would have given a lot to have listened to the conversation between Sharon and her sister after that but I had to be patient. News of that kind travels fast in Clonavon. If Ida didn't find out what happened, I knew Bella would.

Never Too Late

You remember some people for the rest of your life, even if you've only met them briefly. There's no explanation why they stay in your memory while others are forgotten almost before they've moved on. It's the same with some of the call outs I've had. I remember them because they were so tragic or stressful so funny or touching. Sometimes it's a mixture of all of those. Getting a call out to see Hughie McStravick was one of those calls I never forgot.

He was seventy eight years old, dying of cancer. Before his terminal illness, he rarely attended the surgery. I saw him at his home on a daily basis towards the end of his illness. I knew when I called one afternoon that he was dying and it was unlikely he would last the night. His wife Nellie was sitting beside his bed holding his hand. I was struck by the way she looked at him and how attentive she was. It was obvious when she looked at this old man she was seeing something altogether different to what I was seeing – happy memories, tenderness, troubles shared …. Love.

She called me later that evening, around eleven o'clock to say Hughie was agitated and in pain. When I arrived at the house, I found Nellie distraught and tears flowing down her cheeks. I gave Hughie an injection of morphine and waited for it to ease his pain.

A few minutes later, he was more settled though barely conscious. Nellie asked me if I would like a cup of tea. I knew what she really wanted was for me to stay with her until Hughie died. She knew he was near the end. The offer of tea was a way of detaining me.

She brought in a tray of tea and biscuits and sat down by Hughie's bed. She took his hand again and, as she did, I noticed he became much more relaxed. She looked lovingly at his face and it was obvious she loved Hughie McStravick with all her heart and all her soul.

We sat silently for a long time. Nellie occasionally wiped Hughie's brow or a tear from her eye. Hughie was very peaceful. After half an hour I was about to make an excuse and go when she started to talk.

"You know, Hughie mightn't look like much to you now, Dr Griffin but in his day he was the best looking man in Clonavon and for many miles around. We fell in love with each other the first time we met. It really was love at first sight. He was sixteen and I was fourteen. I didn't just fall for him because he was handsome, it was because I felt there was something good about him and I was right. I never cared for anyone else from that day and neither did he."

"You must have had a very happy life together," I said, touched by her sincerity.

"Oh, the happiest. It couldn't have been happier. I married the best man in Ireland."

"And how long have you been married?" I asked, thinking that they must have been together for well over fifty years.

"Eight years," she said.

"Eight years." I repeated trying to keep the surprise out of my voice.

"Yes, eight happy years, the happiest eight years of my life by far."

I didn't say anything for a minute or two but my curiosity got the better of me.

"I thought you said you met when you were fourteen."

"Aye, we did. But Hughie was very shy then and so was I. I knew he was too shy to speak to me and I was too shy to speak to him too. When he was twenty, we happened to be coming out of a ceili dance one night at the same time. I've got to be honest, it didn't just happen by coincidence. I'd been watching him out of the corner of my eye all night. He didn't dance with anyone but I saw him give me the odd shy glance, I knew he couldn't summon up the courage to ask me on to the floor. I told two or three lads who came over and asked me for a dance to go away. I had no interest in them. As far as I was concerned Hughie was the only man for me and I'd no interest in anyone else. When I saw he was getting ready to leave I pretended I was going at the same time. He told me later, when we got married, he'd slowed up to make sure I got to the door ahead of him so we'd meet, accidentally like, outside the door."

"Hello, Nellie Magee," he says to me as we stepped out into the moonlight. "How are you getting on?"

"The very best, Hughie McStravick," I says to him, "and how are you getting along?"

"To tell you the truth, I've never been better in my entire life, Nellie Magee. Did you come to the dance on your bicycle, Nellie Magee?" He always called me by my full name for a joke, even to this day. He said he loved the sound of it."

"I did," I told him, "I came on my bicycle."

"Well, sure, I'll see you safely home."

We both lived two miles from the ceili hall but in opposite directions. We went round to the side of the hall to get our bikes and that was when a few corner boys started calling and jeering and whistling.

"What are you up to McStravick" They started shouting and chanting they were going to tell my Da about Hughie

199

taking me round the back of the dance hall when he thought there'd be nobody there.

Hughie stopped dead in his tracks. He was a very upright man all his life and to be accused of behaving improperly, even by the likes of those corner boys, shocked and disgusted him.

"Wash your filthy mouths out," he shouted at them. I could see he was so angry he would have taken on the lot of them, even if it had meant him getting a beating. They must have sensed his anger because they ran off shouting all the dirty names they could think of at us.

Hughie turned to me and told me he'd better let me cycle home on my own. He said he didn't want my good name destroyed by boys like that. He lifted his cap, got on his bike and cycled off. You can't imagine how bad I felt. I thought my heart was going to break.

After that, he never went to another ceili and, when I saw he wasn't going back, I stopped going myself. Several boys asked me out but I didn't have the slightest interest in them. The only man I wanted was Hughie McStravick and, if I couldn't have him, I didn't want anybody.

We bumped into each other over the years at parish functions or on the street of Clonavon or at wakes and he'd always give me one of his beautiful smiles and say, "Hello Nellie Magee, how are you getting on?" and move on.

Every time I saw him, my heart would miss a beat and I'd be as happy as could be for the rest of the day. It was like being fourteen all over again and falling in love.

We went to the same Mass on Sundays. I could never settle until I saw him coming into the chapel. As soon as he appeared, I'd calm down and be as happy as anything because I knew he was there and I knew he felt the same about me. I spent the whole of the week looking forward to Sunday because I knew I'd see him then if only for a few moments. It kept me going all week. Even though we weren't married, there seemed to be a kind of invisible bond between us."

"So how did you end up marrying Hughie?" I asked.

"Well, I prayed all my life that some day he would get the courage to ask me to marry him. It was about eight years ago we went to a Wake. It was for one of our school friends and, believe it or not, we arrived at the Wake house at exactly the same time. I just knew something was going to happen. I was that excited I could hardly think straight.

We were shown into the sitting room and given a cup of tea. Hughie was given a seat opposite me. There were a lot of people in the room but they began to drift away until there was only the two of us left. I was drinking my tea very slowly praying nobody would be shown into the room. I didn't want the moment to end. I looked at Hughie and saw he was tongue-tied and didn't know what to say. He's an awful shy man. We sat there without saying anything. After a couple of minutes, I heard him clear his throat, I knew he was going to say something.

He put down his tea cup and lifted up the plate of biscuits. "Would you like a biscuit, Nellie Magee?" he asked with that big smile of his that never failed to make my heart skip a beat.

"No thanks, Hughie McStravick," I said and smiled back at him.

"Well then, Nellie Magee, would you ever consider marrying me instead"

I could hear his voice shaking, he was that nervous.

"Yes, I'd consider that alright, Hughie McStravick."

"Would you consider marrying me soon Neillie Magee?"

"Whenever you like Hughie McStravick.".""

"Would next week be too soon for you, Neillie Magee? I think we've delayed long enough as it is."

"Maybe we have Hugh McStravick. Next week would be just fine."

He stood up and shook my hand and said he would have a word with Canon Creen the next day and let me know as soon as possible.

Canon Creen was delighted. "I thought you'd never ask her, Hughie," he said.

It seemed that Hughie had spoken to the Canon several times over the years about wanting to marry me but didn't know how to ask. The Canon had even offered to talk to me himself but Hughie wouldn't hear of it."

I stayed with Hughie and Nellie until the April dawn broke when Hughie died peacefully. Just before he died, he opened his eyes and looked at Nellie with such a look of love, I felt humbled. I left the house as the sun was struggling to rise and the first rays of the day were glistening on the lough. Nellie came to the door and shook my hand and thanked me.

"Do you know doctor, those eight short years I had with Hughie, were better than ten life times with any other man" she said, "I wouldn't exchange them for the world."

As I drove home I couldn't help thinking of Helena D'Arcy. Would she ever say the same thing about me? It was beginning to look unlikely. I knew Helena was the girl for me but did she know it? I would just have to be patient. Unfortunately, patience was a virtue I'd inherited in a very small measure.

An unusual thing happened at Hughie's funeral. It amazed everyone who saw it.

Nellie had a passion for butterflies as far back as she could remember. It was well known she particularly liked Red Admirals.

After Hughie's coffin had been brought into St Mary's for his Requiem Mass, a large Red Admiral flew in through the open door and fluttered up the central aisle and landed softly on Hughie's coffin. It remained there throughout the burial Mass. When the pall bearers came to lift the coffin, it flew to a nearby stained glass window where it stayed.

People used to go into the Chapel to look at the butterfly high up on the vaulted window. After Nellie died, the butterfly disappeared.